The cause of the earthquake is not active fault, but is Hydrogen Implosion

DISC
Publish

The cause of the earthquake is not active fault,
but is Hydrogen Implosion

Copyright © 2020 by Akira Ishida
ISBN 978-4-9911175-0-3 C0082
All right reserved.
Printed in Japan.

Translated from the original Japanese version,
"kyodaijishin-wa-kairisui-no-bakusyuku-de-okoru".
Published by Kougakusha Co., Ltd.
1st printing july., 2013

Book design by Yuki Watanabe

preface

Twenty-five years ago, the author created the essence of "Hydrogen Implosion Theory" the year before retiring from Nagoya Institute of Technology.

Since then, He has pointed out the deficiencies in the current seismology by the "Lecture Activities" and the "Internet".

Why should the textbooks "plate tectonics theory" and "active fault theory" be completely denied, not stop sending out the "Hydrogen Implosion Theory " while receiving criticism?

That is because the "earthquake generation mechanism" described by seismologists is wrong and He is convinced that what is in the textbook is not "scientific truth".

There are still many "unknown parts" about the "Earth" where the Ocean exists.

While the exploration of the Moon and Mars is advancing, the "Shinkai 6500" has been surprised to discover the "sinking continent".

"The sinking of continent " is contrary to the "plate tectonics theory" at the base of seismology.

This indicates the possibility that the "Current seismology" is wrong.

The reason for urgent publication of this book is that seismologists who are members of the "Nuclear Regulatory Commission" are trying to influence the country's critical policy based on the wrong theory of "active fault theory".

As a former professor of civil engineering, we can't just tolerate the "flow" that causes the country to decline.

Now, how unreliable the "Seismology" can be seen in the chart below:

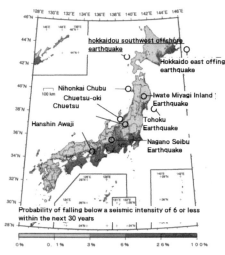

Figure :Probability of experiencing a seismic
intensity of less than 6 within the next
30 years

"Probability of experiencing a seismic intensity of less than 6 in the next 30 years".

If you look at the "Past earthquake example" plotted in this "probability diagram", you cannot be convinced that the next major earthquake will be "three linkages of the Nankai Trough".

Since 1979, "Earthquakes with more than 10 deaths" have all occurred only in "regions where the probability of occurrence is low".

In Japan, where the magma is shallow, earthquakes occur with the same probability at any location.

Prof. Robert Geller, the University of Tokyo, claims that this probability diagram is meaningless, because "earthquake prediction" is impossible, so he screams to stop "prediction research".

However, Professor Geller does not seem to understand the "correct mechanism for earthquakes".

Therefore, we cannot accept the " Guller's Idea" claiming to "stop the earthquake prediction research ".

But why is this ridiculous "probability theory" reported every time? Because they believe in the "wrong seismology theory".

They believe that the "Pacific Plate" and the "Philippine Sea Plate" are subducting under the "Eurasia Plate" . As the "Plate" has not jumped up for nearly 160 years since the "Ansei Tokai Earthquake" (1854), the "Suruga Bay area" and "Nankai Trough Coast" are considered to be "red" . "(Probability 100%).

It was the seismologist's assumption that the "Tokai Earthquake" will occur at least by 2005 at the latest.

This time, it seems that he has escaped to the "Three Linking Theory of Nankai Trough" without being able to give a reason for "the Tokai earthquake not happening".

In other words, they weren't predicting the 2011 catastrophe, so they were probably estimating their predictions larger. In preparation for the "Nankai Trough Triple Earthquake" that may occur in the future, the seismologists would have escaped the responsibility.

However, "plate tectonics" is just one hypothesis, and if the hypothesis is wrong, the probability calculation based on it is meaningless.

In fact, the public was only betrayed.

Now, what is most needed is a "new earthquake cause theory" that replaces "plate tectonics" and "active fault theory".

Therefore, "hydrogen implosion theory" should be widely understood by "politicians", "scholars", "bureaucrats", "citizens", and so on.

There are two main reasons why the author's "hydrogen implosion theory" is rejected by "established authority".

*

----

1.   Misunderstanding of "magma intrusion theory"

In the early Showa period, there was a "magma intrusion theory" by Dr. Mishio   Ishimoto. This theory is completely rejected, and the "explosion" used in the theory is interpreted as a "dynamite-like explosion".

2.   Misconceptions about "the inside of the Earth."

The "mantle" inside the earth is interpreted as "solid".

The details are explained in Chapter 1 and Chapter 2, but "hydrogen implosion" is "implosive explosion".

This is completely different from the "explosion by dynamite".

The "earthquake waveform" clearly shows that the "mantle" is "melting".

First, We will focus on these two points, but there are more important issues.

Carbon Dioxicite Capture and Strage (CCS) is being implemented because it is understood that "CO2 emissions" are the cause of "global warming" . However, it is not understood that this causes an "oxyhydrogen explosion" .

Also, we are not trying to investigate why the "giant tsunami" that destroyed the "Fukushima Daiichi Nuclear Power Plant" struck from the south.

In fact, the "tsunami" occurred in two places.

And "the huge tsunami that hit from the south" may have been caused by the "CCS" that took place off the coast of "Iwaki City" .

Akira Ishida

The cause of the earthquake is not active fault, but is Hydrogen Implosion

by Akira Ishida

Faults are just scars caused by an earthquake.
The underground injection of waste liquid induces an earthquake.

Table of contents

Preface ··· 3
Learn from the starting point, with zero knowledge of earthquakes.

Chapter 1   Explosion Phenomenon ························· 11
[1-1] Why do "earthquakes" occur? ···························· 12
[1-2] "Oxyhydrogen Detonation" (1)("Implosion" cause "pull") ······15
[1-3] "Oxygen hydrogen Detonation" (2)("Energ release" cause "push") …17
[1-4] Is "earthquake classification" meaningful? ···················· 21

Chapter 2   The "inside of the earth" is melting.
At least in the mantle. ························· 25
[2-1] "Mantle melting theory" is proved by "earthquake waveform"… 26
[2-2] Waveform of "near-field and shallow earthquake" ① ······ 27
[2-3] Waveform of "Far-field and shallow earthquake" ② ········ 28
[2-4] Waveform of "Far-field and deep earthquake" ③ ··········· 29
[2-5] "time- distance curve" does not prove "mantle solid theory"… 32

Chapter 3   Mechanism of earthquakes ····················· 37
[3-1] "Earthquake" in the crust (shallow earthquake) ·············· 38
[3-2] Real causes of "earthquake fire" ···························· 44
[3-3] "Earthquake" inside magma (deep earthquake) ·············· 47
[3-4] "Earthquake" caused by "liquid injection" ···················· 54
[3-5] "Chuetsu Earthquake", "Chuetsu Offshore Earthquake" and "CCS" 59
[3-6] Iwate-Miyagi inland earthquake and CCS ···················· 62
[3-7] "Earthquake" associated with "shale gas mining" ··········· 69
[3-8] Other "earthquake occurrence" examples ···················· 70

Chapter 4　Evidence that the earthquake is implosion ··· 73
[4-1] "Jumping stone" phenomenon　……………………… 74
[4-2] "Building hardware" (Holdan) damaged　……………… 74
[4-3] "Sea earthquake phenomenon" and "boat capsize" ………… 77
[4-4] Debris flow and yamatsunami ……………………… 79
[4-5] Sinking of Uryuu Island (horizontal explosion (energy release))　82

Chapter 5　Contradiction of Active Fault Theory　…… 85
[5-1] Contradiction of "active fault" ……………………… 86
[5-2] Meaning of "fault" found after "earthquake"　…………… 87
[5-3] How can the "first fault" be created?　……………… 89
[5-4] From Dr. Kunihiko Shimazaki's "The true nature of the earthquake "　90
[5-5] "Proof assuming existence from the beginning" does not become "true proof"　91

Chapter 6　The Unknown Truth of the Great East Japan Earthquake　……………………………… 93
[6-1] The truth of the tsunami that hit Tohoku　…………… 94
[6-2] There were at least "three explosions" ……………… 97
[6-3] "CCS Project" was underway in "Iwaki City"　………… 98
[6-4] "Two tsunamis" attacked "Fukushima Daiichi Nuclear Power Plant"··· 100
[6-5] Estimate when "tsunami" did not occur "off Iwaki City" … 102

Chapter 7　Macroscopic anomaly mechanism　……… 107
[7-1] Local changes in "Geoelectric current" and "Geomagnetism"　108
[7-2] "Large noise" heard before "earthquake"　…………… 111
[7-3] Local changes in the "surface" and "atmosphere"　……… 112
[7-4] Local changes in the ionosphere　………………… 114
[7-5] Launching phenomenon of "dolphins" and "whales"　…… 116

Chapter 8 Truth of Earth structure ···················· 121

[8-1] The inside of the earth is "Magma Ocean" ·················· 122

[8-2] Controversy between "horizontal" (A) and "vertical" (B) 123

[8-3] What is the difference between the "continental crust"
and the "oceanic crust" ? ··· 124

[8-4] "Floating" of the "continent" (continentalization) ········· 126

[8-5] "Sinking" of the "continent" (oceanization) ·················· 129

[8-6] Failure of "plate tectonics theory" ···························· 132

[8-7] Evidence that tells the rise and fall of the continent ······ 133

[8-8] Contradiction of "isostasy" ·································· 134

[8-9] What the distribution of "rock salt deposit" means ········· 136

[8-10] Deep drilling of the crust is dangerous ···················· 138

[8-11] Seismic region anomaly of "deep earthquake" ············ 141

Appendix 1 ··· 144

Appendix 2 ··· 148

Afterword ·· 152

References ·· 154

Chapter 1

"Explosion Phenomenon"

The phenomenon of earthquakes is still a mystery of mankind,
and the nature of earthquakes is unknown.
The seismologist's commentary on the current theory
is not persuasive.

Therefore, while respecting the superior research of the
predecessor, we must reexamine it from a completely new
perspective and cause an earthquake revolution.
To that end, we want to learn on the basis of
"start from zero base".

We want to bring the knowledge about
earthquakes learned in school education
back to zero and start from scratch.

[1-1] Why do "earthquakes" occur?

Twenty-five years ago, the author, like the readers, believed in "plate tectonics theory" and "active fault theory". He also believed in the explanation of the seismologist on TV.

He did not know that other "earthquake theory" existed in the early Showa period.

① Elastic repulsion
The theory that the "ocean plate" sinks under the "continental plate", and the subducted "continental plate" jumps up without being retained.

②Strain release theory
When the "ocean plate" sinks, "strain" accumulates in the "continental plate". The theory that when this "strain" exceeds a certain amount, "strain energy" is released and an earthquake occurs.

③ Active fault theory
"Strain" is generated when an "ocean plate" sinking near a trench collides with a "continental plate" . The theory that this "strain" is transmitted to the inland, the "active fault" of the "inland plate" moves and causes an earthquake.

It's a vague commentary.

If this theory is correct, if "plate subduction" is the cause of the earthquake, "seismic energy" such as "elastic energy" and "strain energy" after "major earthquake" such as "2011 Great East Japan Earthquake" "Will be released. Therefore, a "new earthquake" (aftershock) will not occur until the next accumulation.

But in fact, the number of "earthquakes" after the "2011 M9 earthquake" has increased considerably.

Japan is also called the "earthquake kingdom" , and many legends remain related to "precursur of earthquake" and "earthquake phenomenon" .

Among them are "Animal Abnormal Behavior" , "Weather Changes" , "Sound Phenomenon" , "Electromagnetic Wave Anomaly" , etc., but the current "Earthquake Theory" cannot explain anything.

Therefore, "folklore" is organized as an "illusion of the ignorant ordinary people" in an era when there is no scientific knowledge of earthquakes.

However, many people have witnessed the "luminescence phenomenon" both in the 1995 Hanshin-Awaji Earthquake and in the 2011 Great East Japan Earthquake.

There seem to be a lot of people who have heard "abnormal noise" and people who have experienced "abnormalities in TV and car navigation".

The books that recorded the signs of the "Hanshin Awaji Earthquake" - [Signs of Prediction 1519!] and [Tangshan Earthquake] (published by the Asahi Shimbun) introduece a variety of phenomena that are called "macroscopic anomaly".

The "Seismic Hydrogen Implosion Theory" published by the author can explain most of the "macroscopic phenomena" scientifically.

*

In the early Showa period, the "magma penetration theory" and "push cone theory" were proposed by Mishio Ishimoto of the Earthquake Research Institute of the University of Tokyo. At that time, there was an air that the earthquake was resolved.

This is the theory that "magma" causes an "explosion" due to "something" and "magma intrusion" between "rocks" is an "earthquake".

The only thing that wasn't clear was the cause of the explosion.

The main theme of this book is that the "cause of the explosion" is the release of energy from the "oxygen-hydrogen implosion" .

*

This "magma invasion theory" has been completely denied by the current "Seismological Society" and is not included in the "Seismology" textbook.

The reason is that if the "earthquake" is an "explosion" (a dynamite-like explosion), the material will be scattered in all directions and will only be "push". In other words, the "explosion theory" cannot explain the "initial push-pull distribution" recorded by the "Seismometer".

"Push-pull distribution" means that the initial movement is "movement approaching the epicenter (pull)" and "movement away (push)" shows a specific distribution.

In fact, this phenomenon can be well explained by Dr. Ishimoto's "Push Cone Theory".

Researchers belonging to the "Authority" of the "Earthquake Society" completely ignore the achievements of Dr. Ishimoto because they misunderstand the following two points.

① They only understand "Oxyhydrogen Detonation" as " dynamite-like explosion".

② They think that "mantle" is "solid", and "flowing" in the long term.

Regarding ②, it is different from the common sense of ordinary people.

Ordinary people will think that "hot springs" will come out everywhere if we dig "underground".

The well-known hot spring resort is just a place where there is a spring source in a shallow place and can be easily digged, and if we dig deep, we will find "hot springs" everywhere.

If we dig deeper, the people think that "magma" will erupt.

However, seismologists belonging to "authority" do not think so.

"The former professor of Kyoto University, Ichiro Kawasaki, says:
Most of the Earth's mantle is undoubtedly solid in the scale of human life, and the mantle is "convective" as a solid.

Therefore, in order to develop the "hydrogen implosion theory" of the author who developed the "Ishimoto theory",

① There are two types of so-called "explosions" : "explosion" and "implosion".

② "Mantle" is "Melting"

You must break through these "two walls".

*

The author doubted "current earthquake theory" when he rewrote his senior paper on "Mysterious story of water".

Among them, there was a description that "water" is not well known.

For example, if you mix "cement" and "water with magnetism", you can make "hard like stone" and "concrete". In addition, it is written that "Sake" will be delicious if you use "that water".

*

What was even more surprising was that when water was exposed to magnetism or high heat, it was written that "water" was separated into "oxygen" and "hydrogen" (in chemical terms "dissociation"). .

Looking at the encyclopedia, there was certainly the word "thermal dissociation", and the relationship between "dissociation degree" and "temperature" under "atmospheric pressure" was displayed as a graph.

＊) In this book, expressions such as Hydrogen Implosion and Oxyhydrogen-Detonation are used, but they have the same meaning: Implosion-Detonation of oxygen and hydrogen.

[1-2] "Oxyhydrogen Detonation" (1) ("Implosion" cause "pull")

At that time the author thought that the only way to make oxygen and hydrogen from water was electrolysis. So when read the sinior paper he thought a considerable amount of "dissociation" had progressed deep in the crust where groundwater meets magma. Then, He thought that, there oxyhydrogen gas is formed,and that the chemical reaction between hydrogen and oxygen would cause oxyhydrogen detonation. It is the cause of the earthquake.

$$2H_2O + (\text{Heat of magma}) \Leftrightarrow 2H_2 + O_2 \cdots\cdots(\text{Implosive Detonation Gas})$$
$$(2 \text{ mol}) \qquad\qquad\qquad (3 \text{ mol})$$

Since then, He have read many books explaining "earthquake outbreakbut only the explanations given by "elastic repulsion theory" and "strain energy release theory".

The only thing he convinced with was Dr. Misio Ishimoto's "Magma Intrusion Theory".

This theory was first conceived by Dr. Takuji Ogawa (Dr. Hideki Yukawa's father). The cause of the explosion was unknown, but explained that the "earthquake" was caused by an explosive "magma intrusion" into the "crack of the rock".

Going back further, we can return to the Humboldt view of earthquakes, where seismic activity and volcanic activity are the same phenomenon.

"Dr. Ogawa" always said, "Return to Humboldt". (Alexander von Humboldt 1769-1859)

Scientist Newton and philosopher Kant also thought the earthquake was an explosion. Even ancient Greek scientists understood that earthquakes are a phenomenon of "gas eruption" that explodes underground.

By the way, in Japan, after World War II, American-born "fault earthquake theory" became dominant.

This is influenced by the declaration of Prof. Keiichi Aki, who once served as the president of the American Seismological Society, " I came back after being brainwashed. Influenced.

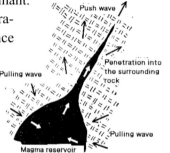

Mishio Ishimoto
(1893-1940)

Fig1-1 Dr. Ishimoto's photo and Magma Intrusion Theory

16

The author is not an expert in "Seismology".

Just before leaving NIT（Nagoya Institute of Tecnology）, he read Dr. Keiichi Kasahara's "Earthquake Science". In this, he first learned about Dr. Ishimoto's magma intrusion theory and push cone theory.

He intuitively understood that these theories were excellent.

The reason is because it explains well the fact that Dr. Toshi Shida found that the initial movements at the time of the earthquake have a regular distribution.

However, most people image the "explosion phenomenon" as a "dynamite-like explosion" that scatters in all directions. Therefore, the "explosion theory" is denied because it is not possible to explain the "pull phenomenon" that is attracted to the epicenter, which will be described later.

In the "Introduction to Modern Seismology" written by Dr. Kasahara in a later year, the research by "Dr. Ishimoto" and others has been wiped out.

*

Now, "Hydrogen Implosion" is not " dynamite-like explosiom", but "implosion" with "volume reduction" in which "volume" changes from "3 mol" to "2 mol". (Implosion).

The "actual mechanism" occurring at the "hypocenter" (seismic source) cannot be explained by the "dynamite-like explosion", but it can be explained if both "implosion" and "energy release" occur simultaneously.

There is no need to use unclear concepts of the physical image, such as "double couple".

[1-3] "Oxygen hydrogen Detonation" (2)
("Energ release" cause "push")

Here, let us briefly explain the mechanism of earthquake occurrence using "schematic diagrams". Details will be explained in Chapter 3.

*

The cause of the earthquake is not active fault,
but is Hydrogen Implosion

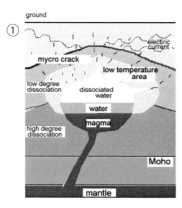

The dissociation layer is usually stable, but moves upwards with decreasing pressure and increasing temperature

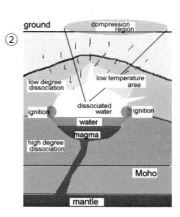

When the degree of dissociation increases, water dissociates, generating dissociated water, and the ambient temperature decreases.

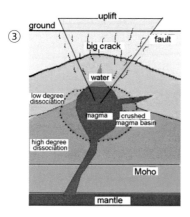

When the temperature returns, an explosion occurs and an earthquake occurs.

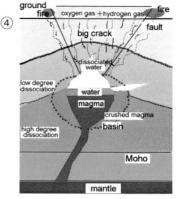

In the binding reaction, the pressure is reduced, the magma chamber collapses, and the magma rises

Fig. 1-2 Mechanism of earthquake occurrence by hydrogen implosion seismotheory

The place where an "earthquake" occurs is a "reservoir storing magma" (magma reservoir), or "an underground space filled with gas".

In short, you should assume an "inside the boiler" that can withstand high pressure.

As "pyrolysis" proceeds, the "pressure" inside the "boiler" increases. During this period, many "predictors of earthquakes" should appear (Fig. 1-2 ②).

When the "Implosion" in Fig. 1-2 ③ occurs, the gas volume decreases immediately. "Boiler destruction", that is, "equilibrium destruction type implosion" occurs.Since this is an "Implosion" , the "direction of energy release" depends on where it is first destroyed.

In the case of a "magma reservoir" , the magma moves through the connecting magma passages and the boiler is destroyed.

This "equilibrium fracture type destruction" is the mechanism of "energy release / explosion".

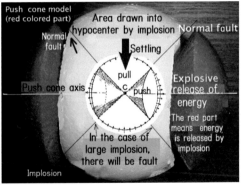

Fig. 1-3 (B) shows a horizontal case.

Fig. 1-3 (A) is a photograph of a three-dimensional model when "explosion (energy release)" is vertical.

In other words, the cause of an "earthquake" is a chemical reaction of water by "heat" released from "magma" in the crust. The cause of the earthquake is the separation of "water" into "oxygen" and "hydrogen" , and "join" to return to "water" .

A "fault" is a "crack" of the earth's crust that could not withstand stress and is "ruptured" as a result of an "explosion (energy release)" .

"Aftershocks" are a phenomenon in which the above "chemical

reaction" is repeated until the dissociation layer is stabilized. The "degree of water dissociation" depends on the relationship between "heat" and "pressure".

"Aftershocks" will not stop until the phenomenon of "thermal dissociation" is stabilized.

When a "big earthquake" or "big implosion" occurs, the "chemical balance" is lost, and "dissociation" and "bonding" occur frequently. This is the "aftershock".

*

When the author understood this, he knew that he had heard the concept explained by the "Seismologist" on television without criticism.

Regarding "subduction of ocean plate", "bounce of continental plate", "friction heat between two plates", "release phenomenon of accumulated strain", etc.

Seismologists misuse two concepts.

The two concepts are ((a) "elastic repulsion phenomenon" and (b) "strain release phenomenon"), which are completely different phenomena.

(a) is "elastic body mechanics" (straight line part in Fig. 1-4), and (b) is "fracture mechanics" (linear tip part in Fig. 1-4).

The nature of "rock" is similar to "glass", and if a "10 meter" object is distorted by "1 mm", it will be "destructed".

Unlike "Steel", "Rock" cannot be used to perform tasks such as "Bounce the opponent's plate".

Both "elastic repulsion theory" and "strain energy release theory" are contrary to basic knowledge of material mechanics.

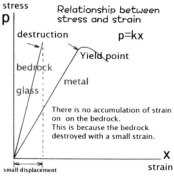

Fig. 1-4 "Strain" and "Stress" have a one-to-one relationship

However, it is difficult to convince people who are obsessed with the problem of "big effects" . Even those who have learned mechanics can easily destroy "Carintou" , but in the case of "Giant Carintou", "Giant effect (?)" Is born and it is difficult to destroy.

In other words, they argue that they cannot be inferred from a test piece like a giant-scale carintou like the "crust" .

Solving the "brainwashing" of "expansion effect" continues to be a difficult task.

[1-4] Is "earthquake classification" meaningful?

There are two types of current earthquake theory.
① Trench-type earthquake
② Inland earthquake (intraplate earthquake)
Then, is there really meaning in "classification of earthquakes" ?

The "trench type" in ① is a "reverse fault type earthquake" and the magnitude of the earthquake is said to be large. In the earthquake of ②, it is explained that the "directly-type" earthquake causes more damage.

There are also words such as "volcanic earthquake","swarm earthquake", "aftershock" , "pre-shock".

In "current theory", the shape of "faults" is explained in various forms. For example, the difference between "normal fault" and "reverse fault", "right lateral fault", "left lateral fault". Some of these shapes are illustrated and implied as if they have significant meaning.

There is no point in classifying "earthquakes" in this way.

"Current seismology" cannot explain why the "direct earthquake" is a terrible earthquake.

According to current theory, all "earthquakes that occur inland" should be classified as "direct earthquakes" .

The meaning of "direct earthquake" cannot be accurately grasped by the "current theory" (see FAQ1-10 of the Seismological Society of Japan), and the meaning is unknown.

As shown in the "3D model" Fig.1-3, the correct interpretation of "directly under the earthquake" is an earthquake whose "energy release" direction is "vertical".

At that time, "pressure" occurs in the "vertical direction".

Therefore, regardless of where the "earthquake" occurs, the "facility" directly above the "hypocenter" will be severely damaged in both "land" and "sea" areas.

If "Explosion (Release of energy)" is horizontal, "Shake damage" will not increase, but "Sinking of the ground" will occur. In the "direct earthquake", just above the hypocenter rises.

The "2011 Great East Japan Earthquake" is close to the "direct type" as shown in Fig 1-5.

In other words, the "explosion at the hypocenter" was "upward" and caused a "big tsunami", but the coastal area that was far from the "seismic epicenter" (just above the hypocenter) became a "pull region" and sank.

As explained in Chapter 5, in the "land area", you can see that the "earth movement" due to the "earthquake" is all going to the epicenter.

In any case, the cause of "earthquake" is the same in terms of "oxyhydrogen explosion".

However, the "explosion direction" has a great impact on the damage to the surface.

In the case of "big implosion", "defects" are created as "scars", but it does not make sense to distinguish fault shapes.

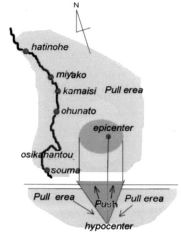

Fig. 1-5 Distribution of "push and pull" in the 2011 Tohoku M-9 earthquake

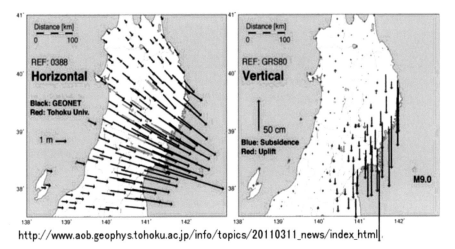

http://www.aob.geophys.tohoku.ac.jp/info/topics/20110311_news/index_html

Fig. 1-6 "Amount of ground movement" in the "2011 Great East Japan Earthquake"

There is no "active fault". A fault is a "scratch" of an "earthquake".

The "causality" between "cause" (earthquake) and "result" (fault) is reversed.

Chapter 2

The "inside of the earth" is melting.
At least in the mantle.

*Geophysics is a research conducted day and night
to elucidate the structure of the earth.
However, university courses are named "Solid Geophysics".
The earth presupposes an understanding of "solid stars".
In the movie "Sinking Japan", Professor Hitoshi Takeuchi of the
University of Tokyo (at that time) explained
that the Earth is a half-boiled egg.
In other words, "Yellow" melts, while "White" mantle is solid.
Geophysical researchers are trying to elucidate
the structure of the Earth from a different perspective
than the common sense.
Furthermore, the fact that the viewpoint is protected by
"academic authority" hinders the progress and development of
geophysics.
Therefore, making "Mantle Melting Theory" the standard
is a truly revolutionary and difficult task.*

[2-1] "Mantle melting theory" is proved by "earthquake waveform"

Next, we will examine the meaning of the "shape difference" that appears in the "earthquake waveform".

The "earthquake waveform" differs greatly between "earthquake that occurred near" and "earthquake that occurred far away", or "when the hypocenter is deep" and "when it is shallow". "Athenosphere" in Fig. 2-1 is defined in " Current Theory". The "Asenosphere" is called "the lower part of the mantle". The "top" is called the "lithosphere".

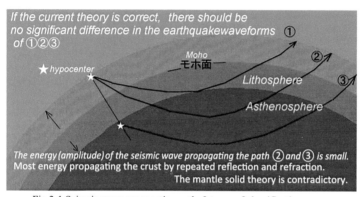

Fig.2-1 Seismic wave propagation path: 3 types of classification

To add for exploration, split the "earth-quake" into three cases as shown in Fig. 2-1. The data for "seismic waves" is bor-rowed from "USGS".

① "Shallow" earthquake that occurred "near"
② "Shallow" earthquake that occurred "far"
③ "Deep" earthquake that occurred "far"

The "crustal definition" of the "current theory" and the "oxygen-hydrogen detona-tion theory" are different as shown in Fig. 2-2.

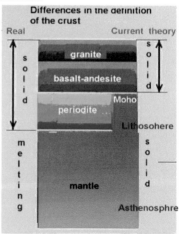

Fig.2-2 Definition of the crust (Current thoryand Oxyhydrogen DetonationTheory)

In the "current theory", the "crust" is defined to be from the Earth's surface to the "Moho boundary".

In the physical sense, it is appropriate to indicate the "solid part" of the crust. Therefore, "Implosive Seismo Detonation Thory" defines the "solid part" of the "upper part" of the "melting mantle" as "crust" .

Furthermore, as shown in Fig. 2-6, the "crust" is divided into an upper "first layer" and a lower "second layer" with "Moho" as the boundary. (The continental crust is roughly divided into "granite" at the top, "basalt" at the center, and "peridotite" at the bottom.)

"Moho" is a "boundary" (Mohorovicic discontinuity surface) where the "propagation velocity" of "seismic waves" changes greatly. It was named because it was discovered by Croatian seismologist "Andria Mohorovicic" in 1909.

In the current theory, the "moho boundary" is recognized as the "crust" .

[2-2] Waveform of "near-field and shallow earthquake" ①

When the hypocenter is shallow and nearby, the "early tremor" arrives first, followed by the "major tremor" .

The "arrival time" on the record can be read near "P" and "S" (theoretical calculation time) in the figure, then both are almost the same as the calculated value.

"Initial tremor" is a "longitudinal wave" like a sound wave and is called "Plimary wave" because it comes first.

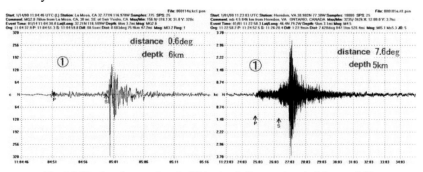

Fig. 2-3 "Earthquake waveform" of "Nearby shallow earthquake" (wave of ①)

The "major vibration" that causes earthquake damage is the "lateral wave" and is called the "secondary wave".

*

A "longitudinal wave" is a wave that moves in the traveling direction of a wave while the medium (the medium that propagates the wave) is pushed or pulled.

On the other hand, "transverse waves" are waves in which the medium moves in a direction perpendicular to the wave travel.

In addition to "earthquake waves", "ocean waves" are also "lateral waves".

Thus, when "hypocenter is shallow", the "distance to the epicenter" (X) can be obtained using the following "Omori formula".

This is the basic equation of "earthquake waves" that we are familiar with.

Omori formula

Vp: Velocity of P wave
Vs: Velocity of S wave
X: Distance from seismometer to epicenter
T: Initial tremor duration

$$X = \frac{Vs \times Vp}{Vp - Vs} \times T$$

[2-3] Waveform of "Far-field and shallow earthquake" ②

The waves of "far field shallow earthquakes" are supposed to pass through a part called Asenosphere. If Asenosphere is "Solid", the waveform should be the same as ①. If not, something is wrong.

Furthermore, unlike ①, "arrival time" and "theoretical calculation time" are not the same, and "P wave" and "S wave" have not reached "calculation time".

Even if it is displayed as shown in Fig. 2-10, which will be described later, you can see that the wave ② has not arrived at the calculated time.

Most energy comes later.

This indicates that the "mantle" is "melted" rather than "solid".

The "inside of the earth" is melting.
At least in the mantle.

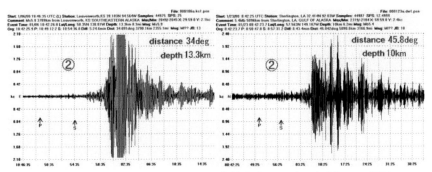

Fig.2-4 "Earthquake waveform" of "Far-field shallow earthquake" (wave of ②)

Therefore, the actual "propagation path" is in the crust, indicating that the refraction and reflection are repeated in the crust.

In other words, instead of passing through the "propagation course" assumed in "numerical calculation" , it means that the zigzag course is progressed and arrives later than the "calculation time" .

"Mantle solid theory" is wrong.

[2-4] Waveform of "Far-field and deep earthquake" ③

③ is completely different from ① and ②.

First, instead of "fine movement" , there is an intense vibration such as "explosion" (the "vertical axis" is exaggerated and expanded.)

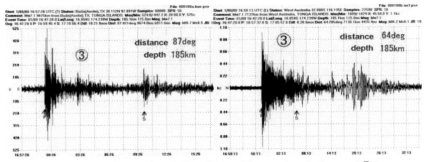

Fig.2-5 "Earthquake waveform" of Far-field and deep earthquake (wave of ③)

However, at first glance, the "arrival time" of the "P wave" seems to match the "calculated value" at first (the same is true for the wave ③ in Fig. 2-10).

29

A feature of "deep earthquakes" is that there is no "big movement" or "damage from earthquakes". The reason why there is a big difference between "shallow earthquakes" and "deep earthquakes" cannot be explained by the "current theory".

This is the same cause as explained in "② Wave".

You can see that the part called "mantle" is "melted" to a depth of at least 2900 km.

In other words, an "explosion" occurs "inside the melting magma". It is the same as "Dynamite Blast" on soft ground and does not function effectively. "S wave" and "surface wave" (main motion) are not generated. If it occurs, it is "small amplitude".

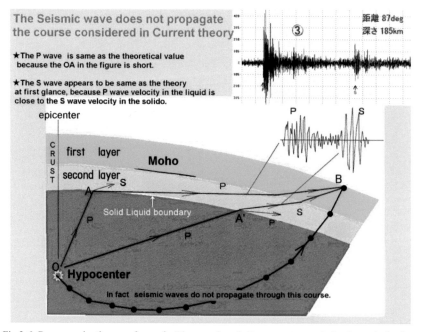

Fig.2-6 Reasons why the waveform of a "deep earthquake" appears to match the theoretical value

The reason why the "arrival time" of the "P wave" appears to match the "calculated value" is that it propagates along the propagation course shown in Figure 2-6. The propagation distance (OA) in the magma is short, and the "P wave" propagates almost through the "solid crust" . As for "S wave" , it seems that "arrival time" and "calculated value" match as "far field" becomes far.

This is because, as shown in Figure 2-6, the "P wave" generated by "explosion (energy release)" is converted to "S wave" by the "crust" and propagates "inside the crust" .

Furthermore, "P wave velocity" propagating through "magma" and "S wave velocity" propagating through "crust" are almost the same.

Therefore, at first glance, both "P wave" and "S wave" appear to be "matched with the calculated value" . Based on that, the "misunderstanding" that "calculated value" and "observation value" actually match even in "deep earthquake" this may be the reason to admit "mantle solid theory" .

In fact, it does not propagate the "curve-like course" considered in the "current theory" .

Since "deep seismic waves" reach the "seismic meter" earlier than the calculated value, problems such as "abnormal seismic area" and "remaining minus travel time" occur.

The fact that "mantle" is "melted" is proved from "earthquake waveform". Nevertheless, those who have studied seismology have been rejected saying "there is no basic knowledge at high school level".They assume that the mantle is solid, but that the light continent is floating above the heavy oceanic mantle.

*

Therefore, it argues that it is impossible to sink a floating light crust.

As a representative, here is a section of the book "What is a slow earthquake" written by Dr. Ichiro Kawasaki, a former Kyoto University professor who is regarded as an "authority of seismology" .

The Earth is sometimes described as melting and becoming "convection" . However, there is no such thing as the "mantle" melts.

In the deep part of the earth, although it is about 1000 degrees Celsius at a depth of 100 kilometers and about 1300 degrees at 200 kilometers, it is about 200-300 degrees lower than the melting temperature of the rocks that make up the mantle.

It's impossible to melt.

A large amount of melted "magma" exists, such as "under the central ridge", which is the source of mantle convection to the surface, or "under the volcano" in a "subduction zone" like the Japanese archipelago. Limited to exceptional places.

Most of the Earth's mantle is definitely "solid" in the scale of human life, and the mantle convects as "solid".

Since this is a "predetermined authority position", authors who deny authority may be in a more severe position than "Galileo in the Church".

*

In this passage, "200 to 300 degrees lower than the melting temperature of the constituent rocks" is the result of melting "basalt" in the laboratory. It shouldn't be an experiment involving water.

Prof. Junzo Kasahara reports that the "melting point" of a substance drops dramatically when "water" is present.

The "Mantle Solid Theory" is only a "useful assumption" when computing the Earth's interior using a computer. In other words, it simply follows the initial calculation method performed by Gutenberg and others.

The "Implosive Sesmo Detonation" defines "the crust" as the "solid part of the Earth", which corresponds to the "raw egg".

In the case of the "current theory", white is considered to be "solidified boiled egg", so it is not clear how far the "crust" is.

In order to avoid complicating the calculation program, the "white" part is also assumed to be "solid", and the physical properties of "solid mantle" are "onion structure". I assume.

Instead of examining the "justification of assumptions", the mantle is regarded as a solid. No one argues about recognizing a mere computational program assumption as a "fact".

[2-5] "time- distance curve" does not prove "mantle solid theory"

The "inside of the earth" is melting.
At least in the mantle.

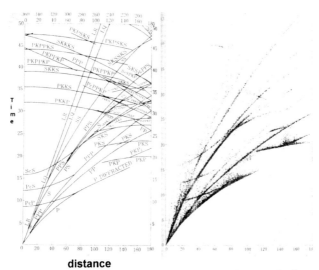

Fig. 2-7 Time-distans table —Theoretical values and measured values

Also, those who reject the "Mantle Melting Theory" are those who think that the "Mantle's Solid Theory" has been proven by the "time- distance curve" .

Is the "theoretical value" and the "observed value" really coincide on the "time- distance curve" ?

If they agree, the "current theory" is correct and the "Implosive Sesmo Detonation" is the wrong conclusion, so the mystery must be solved.

The "travel time table" is an investigation of the relationship between "travel distance of seismic waves" and "time" .

Waves that are complexly reflected by the "inner core" , "outer core" , etc. (such as "P" , "PP" , "S" , "SS") seem to match the "theory" .

*

While investigating this, I found a "retrospective" of an "engineer" who worked for many years to read the "arrival time" from the "record of earthquake" at a university facility.

In the case of "waves far from the epicenter" (waves ② and ③), it is not easy to read where the waves that have been "reflected" or "refracted" inside the earth reach. The "Time-distans table" is an aid to "reading".

33

I found the sentence.

Once the "distance to the epicenter" is known, the "arrival time" of the wave can be read from the "theoretical time-distance table" .

So, if you add that time to the "earthquake time," you can see where it will arrive. Therefore, you can find it by searching around the "time" .

However, this method remains a question as a proof method.

If there is a "wave peak" clearly around the expected time, it can be identified.

But, for example, look at the record of "Far-field and shallow earth-quake" (wave ②) as shown in Fig. 2-8. Can you certify that the "P wave" and "S wave" have arrived at the same time as the "calculated value" (time of "P ↑" and "S ↑" in the figure)?

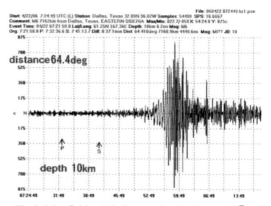

Fig. 2-8 Far-field and shallow earthquake" (wave of ②)

No one will think you can.

In other words, reading from the "earthquake record" must be considered as an arbitrary operation.

*

This method cannot be said to prove the correctness of the theory.

Regarding "Far-field earthquake" in ② and ③, there is a suspicion that "propagation path" is different (not passing through "Athenosphere") even for "P" and "S" .

The author hasn't done any "reading work" from "earthquake records" , so he doesn't know in detail, but not all "reading" is wrong.

The reason is that even if the mantle is melted, the "short-period shock wave" behaves as an "elastic body" .

The "inside of the earth" is melting.
At least in the mantle.

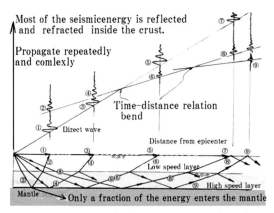

Fig. 2-9 The actual "seismic wave" propagates through
the "crustal interior" in a complex manner

The concept of "rheology" in the "current theory" is "solid" but can be considered as "fluid" in the long term.

However, since the "mantle" (magma) is inherently a "viscoelastic body" , it is a "fluid" , but it behaves as an "elastic body" against "short-period shock waves" . This should be correct.

Therefore, all of "Time-distnce table" is not wrong. However, it is not possible to insist on "mantle solid theory" based on this.

As you can see from the wave ③, the "deep earthquake" is "implosion in the melted magma" , so the energy (amplitude) is "small" .

Also, the wave of ② is different from ①, and "S-wave energy" (amplitude) is very small.

This indicates that the "Athenosphere" can only transmit a fraction of the energy.

Most "energy" propagates in a complicated manner, repeating "refraction" and "reflection" in the crust, as shown in Figure 2-9.

Therefore, it arrives as a "major movement" after a considerable delay.

"Mantle solid theory" is wrong.

*

Fig. 2-10 shows how a "deep earthquake" near Fiji and a "shallow earthquake" near Mariana propagate.

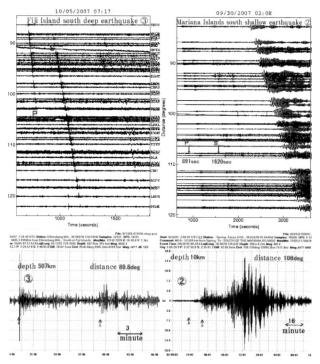

Fig. 2-10 Waveform Comparison of "Deep Earthquake" (③)
near Fiji and "Shallow Earthquake" with Mariana (②)

A "deep earthquake" is a "implosion phenomenon" in the "melting mantle" and clearly shows that there is no "strong vibration" like the "shallow earthquake".

The viewpoint that "the mantle" is melting means a revolutionary "reform" of "geophysics".

The question of whether it is "solid" or "melted" is like the "Battle of the Divine World" in "Geophysics", which is contested over the possibility of "uplifting and sinking of the continent".

Despite the fact that "Shinkai 6500" (the Japanese oceanographic survey ship) has proved this problem, neither "Seismologist" nor "Media" seemed to be aware of the defeat.

Chapter 3

Mechanism of earthquakes

• What is the real cause of the earthquake?
• Why is a big fire caused by a large earthquake?
• Why do earthquakes occur
when "waste liquid" is injected into the ground
when mining underground "oil" or "natural gas" ?

Mankind does not know these causes.
They don't even know that they are "ignorant"
about the truth of earthquakes.
The United States, who is pleased
with the mining of "shale gas",
may have great regrets in the future.
It is hoped that the people will know the correct mechanism
of earthquakes and operate the country wisely.

[3-1] "Earthquake" in the crust (shallow earthquake)

It proved that the "mantle" was "melted", that is, "melted magma" existed everywhere under the "crust".

Here, we will explain the "earthquake mechanism" that occurs in the crust.

*

In fact, in the "current plate theory", "Melting magma" is supposed to exist only in the following three locations, as previously mentioned by Dr. Ichiro Kawasaki.

① Trench
A place where the "plate" is submerged and generates "friction heat" with the "continental plate", and the rocks that make up the plate are "melted" by the "heat".
② Sea ridge
Where "plates" are born
③ Hot spot
A special place like "Hawaii Island"

This may be quite different from the image of citizens.

*

In the citizen's image, if you dig deeper into the ground, you may feel that hot springs are everywhere, and if you dig deeper, "magma" exists.

"Opinion of seismology" based on "current theory" is strange even from the public's perspective.

In countries with volcanic belts such as "Japan" and "Indonesia", "magma" is approaching "shallow places". In other words, it is like floating on the "magma ocean".

For this reason, it is not strange when an earthquake occurs "when" or "where".

However, it is not logical to say that the Tokai earthquake is irrelevant at any time because it has not bounced for the last 150 years.

*

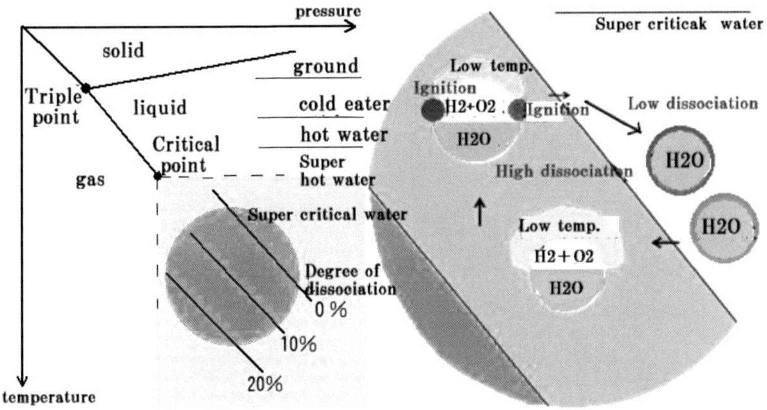

Fig.3-1 Conceptual diagram for explaining the concept of "three states" (solid, liquid, gas) of water and thermal dissociation.

Fig. 3-1 is a diagram for explaining the concept of "three states" (solid, liquid, gas) of water and thermal dissociation.

The deeper the "groundwater" , the more it changes from "cold water" to "warm water" , "hot water" , and "supercritical water" . At that time, depending on the "temperature" and "pressure" , the "thermal dissociation reaction" described above takes place and separates into "oxygen" and "hydrogen" .

The degree of "separation" (dissociation) is higher as "pressure" is lower, and higher as "temperature" is higher.

*

The "dissociation degree" "high and low" is schematically shown as "oblique line" in Fig. 3-1.

Since it is a "supercritical state" , it is considered that it actually exists in an "ionized" state—that is, a "plasma state" .

*

Here, it is assumed that there is a "water mass" that "moves" from an environment with a low degree of dissociation to a high environment.

The "bound water" whose "dissociation degree" was "low" partially changes to "dissociated water" under the "high environment" .

Since this "chemical reaction" is an "endothermic reaction" , a "low temperature region" extends to the "water mass" . In other words, the "hydrogen" that makes up the "dissociated water" does not immediately cause a "detonative reaction" . However, if the temperature moves from the surroundings after a while, the "low temperature range" will shrink
In addition, the "water mass" recovers to the "ignition temperature" of "hydrogen gas" . Then, it "ignites" , becomes "occurrence of earthquake" , and returns to "bonded water" again.

As you can see, when a "big earthquake" occurs, the reactions shown by the "arrows" occur cyclically, and the "aftershock" will "continue" indefinitely.
This is schematically shown as "magma chamber" in the "boiler interior" as shown in Fig. 1-2, "Earthquake mechanism diagram" in Chapter 1.
The following explanation is based on Figure 1-2 in Chapter 1.

~~~~~~~~~~~~~~~~~~~~~~~~~~~~~~

[1] Normally, as shown in Fig. 1-2 ①, a zone with the same degree of dissociation (equal dissociation degree line) exists stably, so there is no cause for earthquakes.
When a "pressure drop" (low pressure) or "temperature rise" (magma rise) occurs, the "isodissociation curve" also rises.

[2] When the "iso-dissociation degree line" rises, the "magma water" inside the "magma chamber" starts "dissociation" and the "dissociation water" increases (Fig.1- 2 ②).
Since this is an "endothermic reaction", the "temperature" will drop once. During this period, various "Signs of the earthquake" should appear.
"Ground current" is also generated by "crack" in "rock" due to "high

pressure".

Furthermore, if the "dissociated gas" in the "plasma state" moves, a geocurrent flows, "MHD power generation" occurs, and a local geomagnetic anomaly occurs.

"High pressure" can cause "hot water" to erupt, creating a hot and humid atmosphere.

An "animal" that senses "earth current" or "electromagnetic waves" may behave abnormally. There may be "abnormal radio waves" that can cause the aircraft to become uncontrollable.

In the "Tangshan earthquake", there is also a sighting that "the building rebars that were placed on the ground emitted a spark".

The more "abnormalities" appear, the more you need to be wary of "giant earthquakes".

Traditional legends cannot be explained by the scientific knowledge of that era, but they are not "mistakes" but often just because science was underdeveloped.

[3] Next, when the "temperature" recovers due to "thermal conduction", the "ignition temperature" of "hydrogen" is reached and "oxyhydogen detonation" occurs.

In the state as shown in Fig. 1-2 ③, it is the "magma channel" that the "boiler" breaks, that is, the "top" and "bottom". "Equity failure type" (Energy release) is "upward" and "downward", and "Implosion" is "horizontal" (Fig. 1-3 (A))..

By examining the "Seismometer" on the ground, you can see the direction of the first movement (initial movement) of the "earthquake".

This distribution is called "initial push-pull distribution".

The person who first discovered this was "Toshi Shida". This distribution is well explained by Dr. Mishio Ishimoto's "Push cone theory" shown in Fig. 3-2.

Here, push-cone theory is explained.

The cause of the earthquake is not active fault,
but is Hydrogen Implosion

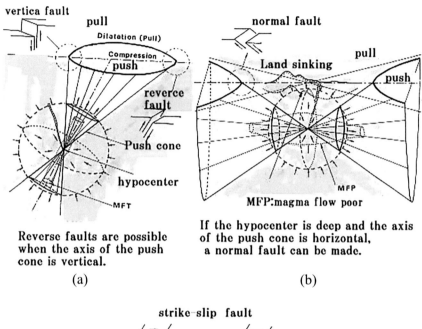

Reverse faults are possible
when the axis of the push
cone is vertical.

(a)

If the hypocenter is deep and the axis
of the push cone is horizontal,
a normal fault can be made.

(b)

If the hypocenter is shallow
and the axis of the push cone
is horizontal, a strike-slip fault
is generated.

(c)

Fig.3-2   Depending on the slope of push-cone and the depth of hypocenter, the type of fault changes

Fig.3-2 (a) If "axis" of "push cone" is close to "vertical", "reverse fault" will occur and it will be an earthquake with severe damage called "direct earthquake".

Fig.3-2 (b) If the "axis" is close to horizontal, a "normal fault" will occur.

Even if "hypocenter" is directly below, it is not a "direct earthquake", so the earthquake damage is not significant, but "sedimentation of the ground" occurs.

The "Uryuu island sank" in Beppu Bay and the "Kuroda-gun sank" in Tosa Bay are thought to have occurred because the area was in the "pull area".

Fig.3-2 (c) When "axis is horizontal" and "hypocenter is shallow", the "fault", which is a scar, becomes a "horizontal misalignment fault".

When the other side is shifted to the "right", it is called the "right shift fault", and when the other side is shifted to the "left", it is called the "left shift fault". However, it doesn't make much sense to distinguish.

----

[4] Due to the "chemical reaction" that is "imlosion detonation", the "boiler" is depressurized and crushed. Once lowered, the "magma" will rise again. (Fig.1-2③)

"Uplift" is seen on the "earth surface", and "tsunami" will occur on the "sea floor". If the explosion is vertical as shown in this figure, it will be a push wave that "the first wave of the tsunami goes up".

If the "explosion" is horizontal, the "first wave" of the "tsunami" becomes the "pulling wave".

Actually, a terrible thing happens after this. The horror of "earthquake fire". Have you noticed that this state is similar to the original state (Fig. 1-2 ①)?

Here, the generation of "Oxyhydorogen gas" is resumed. However, this time, "crack" has appeared at the top of the hypocenter (Fig. 1-2 ②), so "dissociated gas" or "superheated steam" will be ejected on the ground.

~~~~~~~~~~~~~~~~~~~~~~~~~~~~~~~~~~~~~

This can cause an "earthquake fire".

[3-2] Real causes of "earthquake fire"

This is the real cause of "fire" in the "big earthquake" .

The author heard that firefighters extinguished many times during the 1995 Kobe earthquake. They said they were very tired because they did not extinguish the fires, and they had to do fire fighting over and over again.

In the "1993 Okujiri Island Earthquake" , Aonae's fishing port "fired" and became a big fire, despite being flooded by the tsunami.

Japan may have vaguely thought that "it is easy to start a fire if an earthquake occurs" because of many "wooden houses" .
However, the "1906 San Francisco earthquake" , which had many stone houses, also caused a "big fire" .

The same applies to "Tornado" and "Typhoon Disaster" in that the house is completely destroyed. However, compared to other disasters, in the case of an earthquake, the greater the earthquake, the greater the fire. As explained above, the truth cannot be grasped without understanding that an earthquake is an "implosion phenomenon" of "dissociated gas" .

Dr. Hitoshi Takeuchi, who was a "a famous plate tectonics introducer in Japan" , did not know the "cause of the fire" and made the following inappropriate comments in his book.

This is the idea of "group evacuation" planned in Tokyo.
For example, people living near my house are supposed to evacuate to Komazawa Park in the event of an "earthquake" .
The meaning of "evacuation" is misunderstood. People think that immediately after the "Great Tokyo Earthquake," they stop origin of a fire, and after they lock the house, all the people in the town move to a collective evacuation site. Yes. In

addition, training that makes you think so is done.

In my opinion, this is a detrimental and unprofitable way. What residents should do after turning off their homes is to fight the fire that comes to their homes or areas. It is annoying to leave the digestion to the fire department and have them evacuate.

The collective shelter itself is dangerous. During the "1923 Great Kanto Earthquake," about 40,000 people who had been evacuated together were burned dead.

(From Hitoshi Takeuchi "The Way to Become a Creative Man" p.140

Dr. Takeuchi is respected as an "authority of earthquake" , so you may want to keep his advice. However, if a "great earthquake" occurs, it is important to evacuate to a safe place as soon as possible.

In the case of a "large earthquake" , hot gas may be ejected from a crack caused by an explosion in the "push cone" even if it is far from the "seismic center" .

Therefore, you should think that "fire" is inevitable.

Those who experienced "earthquakes" and "fires" at "Aonae Fishing Port" said, "When turning around, a " bulk of fire " on a black shadow came to the shore, hit the house and burned up." He says.

There is a story about "fire" at the same time as "earthquake", and if you escape late, you will lose your life.

The author thinks it's better to forget about protecting the house.

By the way, I will introduce the "dynamic model" in "hypocenter" called "double coupling" , which was discussed in Chapter 1.

This was proposed to explain the mechanism of the "push-pull distribution" of "initial movement" . However, it is just an idea that "physical image" cannot be grasped at all.

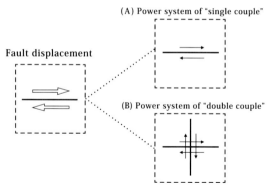

Fig 3-3 "Single couple" and "Double couple"

  Dr. Ishimoto's "Push Cone Theory" can be easily understood and convinced. However, according to Dr. Ishimoto, this "couple theory" can be presumed to be rejected as "conceptual play".

  In short, there should be no deviation unless "opposite force" acts on both sides of the "fault" as shown in Fig. 3-3. Here, "opposite force" means a couple of forces acting on "hypocenter".
  Whether to consider this "couple" as "two sets" or "one couple"?
This has long been an academic debate, and eventually the "two (double) couple theory" was recognized. However, if "push cone theory" is adopted, it becomes meaningless.
  Although it can be processed in terms of mathematical formulas, it is difficult to grasp as a "physical phenomenon".
  This concept is ignored in "Oxyhydrogen Detonation Theory (Implosive Seismo Detonation)".
  In "hypocenter", if "two couples" are set to work, it is easy to process mathematically.

*

  Regarding "Humboldt's view of earthquake", which was discussed in Chapter 1, "Dr.Takuji Ogawa" used to say "Return to Humboldt". Dr. Ogawa would have said, "Be sure to understand the phenomenon physically before using mathematics". Humboldt made his remarks after conducting extensive field surveys of the volcano and being physically familiar with natural phenomena.

Humboldt estimated that "volcanic activity" and "earthquake activity" are the same phenomenon.

He thought that the "explosion" that occurred in the deep underground (the meaning is different from "deep" in Current theory) was an "earthquake" , and the "explosion that occurred in a shallow place" was "volcanic activity" .

So he thought that "volcano" was a "safety valve" for a huge earthquake.

Looking at the "earthquake" from the latest "Oxyhydrogen Detonation Theory" , the normal "volcanic earthquake" is considered to be "Implosion in magma" . However, "mountain collapse" like Mt. St Helens also includes "steam explosion" . Because it is shallow from the ground surface, it seems to be a phenomenon that instantaneously changes from "liquid phase" to "gas phase".

In that sense, "earthquake" and "volcano" may not be exactly the same phenomenon.

However, since this is a phenomenon related to relatives, "Seismologists" and "Volcologists" would like to work together.

[3-3] "Earthquake" inside magma (deep earthquake)

Next, consider "earthquakes" (deep earthquakes) inside the magma.

In the "current theory" , the concept of "phase transition" is sometimes used, but it is not solved.

Since there is no "solid wall" structure like "boiler" inside the magma, the power of Explosion is reduced, and "Implosion" is the driving force of the earthquake.Therefore, on a scale, there are fewer cases of "earthquakes" that cause damage.

"Earthquakes in magma" occur in "deep places" of "600 to 700 kilometers" .In the "current theory" , earthquakes that occur at a depth of "60 to 300 kilometers" are called "slightly deep earthquakes" , and those that occur deeper than "300 km" are called "deep earthquakes" ..

However, the number "300km" has no special meaning.

Rather, the physical meaning becomes clearer when it is divided into earthquakes that occur "inside the crust" and earthquakes that occur "inside the mantle" .

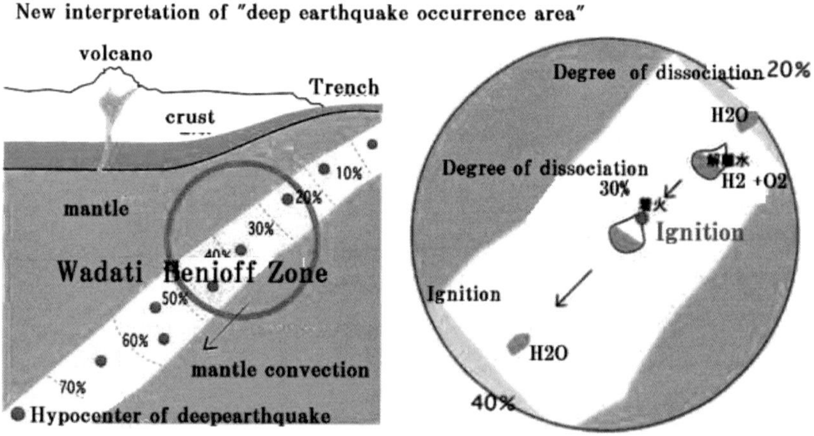

New interpretation of "deep earthquake occurrence area"

Fig. 3-4 Schematic diagram of the mechanism of earthquakes occurring
inside the magma (deep earthquake)

Now, in the "current theory" , the "deep earthquake surface" named "Wadachi-Benioff Zone" is considered to be the place where the plate is subducted.

However, Hydrogen Implosion suggests that it means a "seismic distribution map" of earthquakes inside the magma.

48

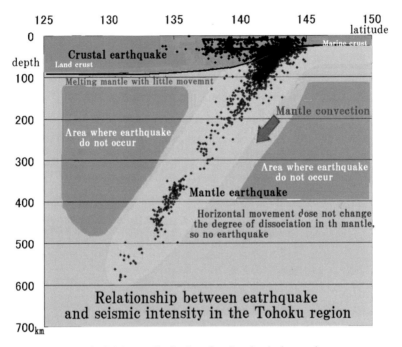

Fig. 3-5 Source distribution of earthquakes in the mantle

In "Hydrogen Implosion" , this is interpreted as showing evidence that "magma" (melting mantle) is "convection" .

The "magma" (melting mantle) inside the earth rises from the deep underground at the "central ridge" of the ocean, moves horizontally to the "trench" , and finally sinks into the "inside the earth" .

It sinks diagonally in the "Japan Trench" , "Kuril Islands Trench" and "West Coast of South America" , but in "Ogasawara" and "Near Mariana" it sinks vertically. In other words, it is as "magma" , not as "plate" .

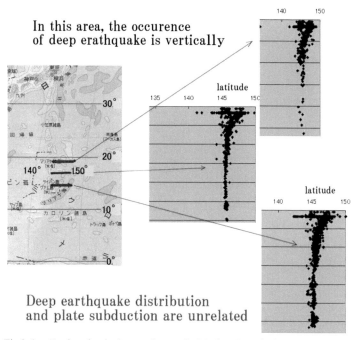

In this area, the occurence
of deep erathquake is vertically

Deep earthquake distribution
and plate subduction are unrelated

Fig.3-6   Earthquakes in the mantle near the Mariana Trench (deep seismic surface)

So-Calld "deep earthquake surface" is the "seismic source distribution" of the "earthquake" (implosion) that occurs in the flow of this "magma" .

The "subduction" described in the "current theory" is not true.

*

At the Pacific Ridge, the "magma" inside the Earth emerges while repeating "earthquakes" .

Every time an "earthquake" occurs, the "bound water" increases, so the final result is mostly "bound water" . Next, the magma moves horizontally.

When moving horizontally, "pressure" and "temperature" are constant, and "dissociation degree" does not change. Therefore, except for the places where "submarine volcanoes" exist, "earthquakes" usually do not occur on "ocean ocean floors" .

When the magma reaches the "trench" and begins to "submerge" , the "dissociation ability" (the ability to "dissociate" water) increases as the temperature rises. (In fig.3-7, it is indicated as dissociation power)

If it sinks as "laminar flow" , "dissociation" increases within the limit of "dissociation ability" , "bound water" decreases, and "hydrogen implosion" does not occur. However, in nature, it sinks as a "turbulent flow" and creates a "vortex" . When returning locally, "dissociated water" exceeding "dissociation ability" may cause "implosion" and return to bound water. This is a "deep earthquake" .

Eventually, all the "bound water" is replaced by "dissociated water" around the deepest "depth 700km" where "deep earthquakes" occur.
The fact that there is no "deep earthquake" at a depth exceeding "700 km" means that this region is the limit that can exist as "H2O".

*

Next, the relationship between the ratio of "dissociated water" and bound water (H2O) in "magma" and "earthquake" are shown in a schematic diagram. (The dissociated water is "mixed gas" of "H2" and "O2")

We will consider the case where the Earth's interior moves from "A → B → C → D" along the convection of the "magma" (melting mantle).

The cause of the earthquake is not active fault,
but is Hydrogen Implosion

Fig. 3-7(a) Generation of vortices when magma flows as turbulent flow

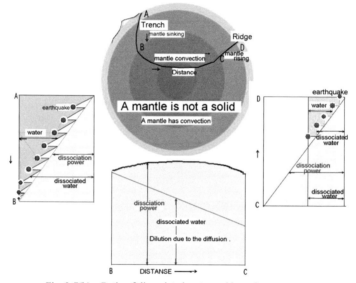

Fig. 3-7(b)   Ratio of dissociated water and bound water
in the mantle (melting magma) (conceptual diagram)

A → B

When sinking from "A → B" , "magma" containing combined water formed by "inner crust earthquake" near the "trench" sinks.

If you sink in a "laminar flow state" , it will sink without causing an "earthquake" , and "bound water" will simply be converted to "dissociated water" .

However, since it flows as "turbulent flow" in the natural world, the part once submerged in the "deep part" may locally "float" (return) due to the "vortex" . (Fig.3-7 (a))

Then, the "dissociated water" "dissociated" in the "deep part" exceeds the "dissociation ability" in the "shallow part" , so the excess "dissociated water" causes "hydrogen implosion" and an earthquake occurs.

Then, it returns to "bonded water" again and begins to "sink" again.

In this way, "earthquakes" are repeated over and over and replaced with "dissociated water" .   When it reaches "B point" , it becomes all "dissociated water" ("H2" and "O2" state or "ionized" "plasma" state).

Therefore, it can no longer exist in the "bonded state" of "H2O" .

This is the "occurrence limit" of "deep earthquakes" .

B → C

From "B to C" , it becomes "horizontal convection" .
"Point B" contains "dissociated water" up to the limit of "dissociation ability" , but "diffusion phenomenon" occurs during "convection" toward "point C" . It can be diluted.

When the "C point" is reached, it contains "dissociated water" that is well below the "dissociation ability" .

C → D

Although it rises from "C point", since it contains only "dissociated water" rather than "dissociation ability", there will be no earthquake for a while.

At a certain depth, it contains "dissociated water" that exceeds "dissociation ability" . At that time, "dissociated water" exceeding "dissociation ability" causes improsion and is converted to bound water.

When it reaches the bottom of the crust, most is replaced with bound water. This "bonded water" becomes "supercritical water", "dissolves" and "a large amount of metal".

This is the essence of the "black smoker" seen near the ridge.

The reason there are sediments on the seabed is that various metals are deposited from this combined water.

In the NHK program, there was an explanation that the seawater that permeated from the surrounding sea floor became hot water by the heat of magma and erupted. But this is wrong.

*

From the above explanation, you should be able to understand scientifically that deep earthquakes occur in the trench but only   shallow earthquakes occur in the ridge.

Even in onshore, if a   magma ascending phenomenon occurs locally in the volcano, a swarm earthquake will occur. As a result, the   outflow phenomenon of groundwater and the accompanying landslide phenomenon occur.

The Matsushiro earthquake swarm that lasted for five and a half years since 1965 is a typical example of the above.

[3-4] "Earthquake" caused by "liquid injection"

It must be recognized that an "earthquake" occurs even if "liquid" is injected into the "deep place" .

*

This phenomenon was first noticed because the "waste liquid" was injected underground in the "Munitions Factory" of "Denver" in the United States.

This is a very famous story. In 1962, in the "Nuclear Factory" of "Denver" in the United States, "nuclear contaminated water" was put under pressure into the "underground" .

At a depth of "4000 meters" .

Then, "earthquakes" began to occur several times a month.

In response to this incident, the residents raised their voices saying "it was strange," and when the "injection of waste liquid" was stopped for one year, the "earthquake" subsided considerably.

When the waste solution was injected again, the "earthquake" began to occur again.

This time, it was a "giant earthquake" that caused damage to the house.

Based on these cases, it is forbidden to put "liquid" into the "underground" in the the vicinity.

However, they don't know the reason why "when " liquid " is put into " underground " , an earthquake occurs." Japanese seismologists also put "water" It is interpreted that "bedrock" became slippery. (Dr. Hitoshi Takeuchi writes in his book.)

As shown in Fig. 3-8, there is a clear correlation between "Waste fluid injection volume" and "Number of earthquakes".

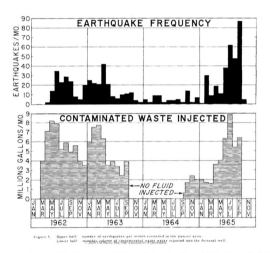

Fig. 3-8   Relationship between "Water Injection" and "Earthquake" in "Denver"

However, since there is no correct understanding of "why an earthquake occurs", a mysterious story has been born. For example, "If water is added, the fault will be slippery and cause an earthquake" or "Small earthquakes can be used to dissipate the energy stored in a huge earthquake." Something like the "Hydro-earthquake theory" is born.

At that time, it was said that there was no "earthquake" in the vicinity of Denver for 80 years. Therefore, it is impossible to have accumulated "giant energy" .

By applying "pressure" and injecting "water", a new earthquake occurred.

Recently, "earthquakes" are frequently generated by mining "shale gas". For this mining, it is necessary to send "water" at "high pressure" and "crush" the shale, so sending "high pressure water" can change "pressure in the deep underground". May have induced "water dissociation".

January 1,2000 to March 31,2004
M4.5 or more,dpth 100km or less

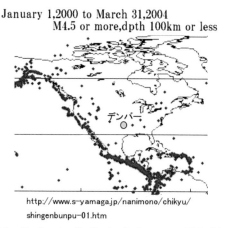

http://www.s-yamaga.jp/nanimono/chikyu/
shingenbunpu-01.htm

Fig. 3-9   Earthquake distribution in the western United States

"Changing the degree of dissociation" means "promoting the generation of hydrogen" and "producing" an "earthquake".

*

During the writing of this book (May 27th), the earthquake disaster in Arkansas was reported.

(CNN) 2013.05.27 In Central Arkansas, the "unknown cause of vibration" has occurred "more than 30 times" several days ago, and residents are worried.

The expert said on the 26th that the link to "natural gas exploration" being conducted nearby cannot be denied.

Unexplained tremors occurred one after the other in the area centered in the state's central Mollington.
It was the largest, and the magnitude (M) 3.5 shake was observed on the night of

the 22nd, and the shake of "M3.4" was observed on the night of the 23rd.

Mr. Scott Ausbrooke, an expert at the Geological Survey of the state, does not do know whether this "shake" is an "earthquake" or "another cause" He said that it is "probably the same as a very expensive lottery" that a lot of shaking will occur in a short period of time. He also pointed out, "It is unusual for four separate areas in the state to occur in the same week."
The magnitude of the vibration is such that things on the shelf shake rattlingly, but there is no doubt that it continues to shake as much as people feel.

In the same state, "more than 200 times" "shaking" was repeated two years ago, and the state of "shake" subsided when the state stopped the new "injection well" .

According to Mr. Ousbruck, some of the areas where this "shake" is occurring are "injections" that are outside the scope of the injunction and are still in operation. Some locations are only about 13km away from the well.

On the other hand, the basis of the "earthquake theory" is that the fault running through this region is very curved and "strain is expected to accumulate," says Mr. Ausbrook.

They don't have the correct knowledge of "earthquakes" , so they don't know the "cause of shaking" .

*

"Denver" and "shale gas mining area" are "central part of the continent" and away from the "volcanic belt" , so "magma" is in the "deep part" .
Therefore, applying "pressure" and "sealing liquid" does not constitute a "giant earthquake" .
However, in "Japan" , where "magma" is approaching "shallow places" , it will be difficult without careful consideration.

By the way, it seems that project managers recognize that "CCS (Carbon dioxide capture and strage) technology" is a technology that has been put to practical use overseas and has been recognized globally.
However, what is put into practical use is in places where the "crust" is "thick" like the "continental crust" .

In countries belonging to the "volcanic belt" , such as "Japan" and "Indonesia" , the "crustal thickness" is "thin" , and the "melt mantle" exists just below the "crust" .

Therefore, it is necessary to know that adding an artificial hand to the "deep depth" leads to "changing the degree of water dissociation" and increases the "risk of earthquake occurrence" .

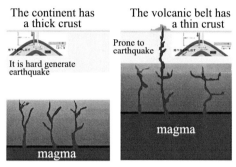

Fig. 3-10 "Crust thickness" relates to "earthquake risk" and "earthquake scale"

You can clearly see that both are "central areas of the continent" or "places away from the volcanic belt" .

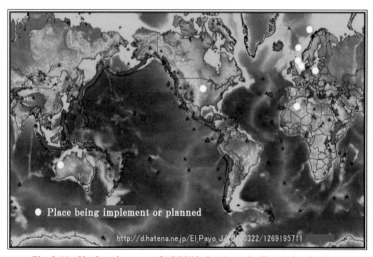

Fig. 3-11 Site location map of "CCS" being "practical" or "planning"

[3-5] "Chuetsu Earthquake", "Chuetsu Offshore Earthquake" and "CCS"

Three months after the "Chuetsu Earthquake" (October 23, 2004), the following e-mail was sent from the reader of the site.

In the "Chuetsu earthquake" , "strong aftershocks" occurred many times, and it continues to be weakening.

The other day, NHKTV reported on an experiment to reduce the amount of CO2 released into the atmosphere to prevent global warming. From July 2003 to January 2005, an experiment to send CO2 into the "aquifer covered with bedrock" called "Cap Rock" in the upper part of Nagaoka City, about 1000 meters below the ground.

Until then. For details, please refer to [Research Institute for Global Environmental Industry (RITE)].

In this experiment, "CO2" enters the gap in place of the "water" contained in the "aquifer" gap, but what will happen to the "water" expelled? .

There is an article called "Denver water injection experiment" in "22" http://www.ailab7.com/lib_022.html#lcn022 of the library, but I think it is the same action.

Isn't it the cause of "strong earthquakes" going on so many times?

I would appreciate your feedback.

The author was surprised to learn about the "CCS" (carbon dioxide capture and storage plan) experiment conducted near the epicenter.

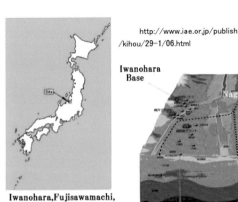

http://www.iae.or.jp/publish /kihou/29-1/06.html

Iwanohara Base

Nagaoka

Iwanohara,Fujisawamachi, Nagaoka
Teikoku Oil "MInaminagaoka Mine"

Fig. 3-12 Iwanohara Base in Fukasawa, Nagaoka City, Niigata Prefecture (CCS experiment site)

Immediately, the author sent an e-mail to the project manager of "Global Environment, Industrial Technology, and Research Organization" (RITE) as the director of "Ishida Earthquake Research Institute" and appealed about "the danger of CCS". However, the person in charge did not seem to be aware of the danger at all.

According to "Hydrogen Improsion Seismo Theory", "CO2 underground injection work" is an operation that artificially promotes "thermal dissociation of water" and causes a "earthquake". Already, it has been proven by "Denver waste liquid injection" and "Waste liquid injection work in shale gas mining".

In the reply from the project manager, there were three objections starting with the following sentence.

> Please provide appropriate opinions and responses based on scientific grounds, not speculations from overseas cases (Denver) with completely different geological and geophysical conditions.

At the end of the sentence,

> Regarding the research and development of this project, discussions based on scientific grounds were carried out by teachers of academic experts at the "CO2 Geological Storage Research and Development Promotion Committee" chaired by Professor Emeritus of the University of Tokyo. I would like to add that we are promoting demonstration testing.

It was written. Since it is clear that he is relying on "established authority", the reply from the author is written as follows.

> No matter what scholars you have, all of you are unskilled in unknown sciences, so you would say, "At that time, scholars did not know."
> As mentioned above, even if the scholar's testimony exempts legal responsibility, moral responsibility may remain.
> I am most worried that the knowledge about the cause of the earthquake may be wrong, which may lead to a lot of tragedy, with easy human engineering in the deep

underground. .
I hope you will reconsider the above.

"Three items of objection" and "author's reply" from the project manager are listed at the end of this book as Appendix 1 "Safety awareness of RITE CO_2 geological storage plan (CCS) manager".

If you are interested, please read it and use it as a reference for building your own opinion.

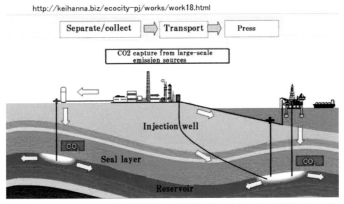

http://keihanna.biz/ecocity-pj/works/work18.html

Fig. 3-13 Illustration of "CCS Operation" in "Land Area" an d "Sea Area"

On July 16, 2007, the "Chuetsu offshore earthquake" occurred. The epicenter of the Chuetsu Earthquake is point-symmetric with respect to the "Iwanohara Experiment Station" (Fukasawa).

NHK reported "Professor Ichiro Kawasaki" of the Disaster Prevention Research Institute at Kyoto University, "It was an earthquake that occurred due to the release of the strain caused by the Pacific plate pushing the Eurasian plate".

In the same NHK news, a resident of Kariwa village talked about their experiences with the expression "flew away" rather than "vibration".

In the previous "Chuetsu earthquake", some people have witnessed that the radish in the field has slipped off like a rabbit.

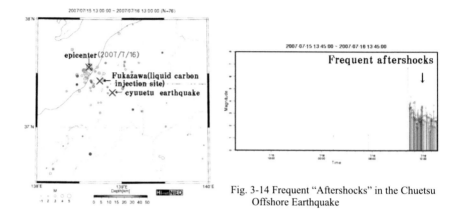

Fig. 3-14 Frequent "Aftershocks" in the Chuetsu
Offshore Earthquake

The Yomiuri Shimbun reported that the acceleration indicating the intensity of shaking was "1500 gal".

Even after experiencing two "damaging earthquakes" in 2004 and 2007, seismologists' perceptions did not change from "plate theory" or "active fault theory".

[3-6] Iwate-Miyagi inland earthquake and CCS

On June 14, 2008, this time suffered a major "earthquake disaster" called the "Iwate-Miyagi Inland Earthquake", which recorded acceleration exceeding 4,000 gal.

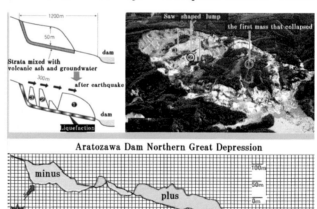

Fig. 3-15 Major collapse of "Northern Aratozawa Dam" in the "Iwate-Miyagi Inland Earthquake"

In the north of Aratozawa Dam, a mountain tsunami appears as if it had collapsed due to an underground explosion.

At the same time, the author found out that the "CCS Project" was being carried out at the "Ogachi Experiment Station" in Akita Prefecture by e-mail from readers of the site three months later.

It was an e-mail asking for an explanation from the standpoint of "Implosive Seismo Detonation" on the news of "CCS Experiment" published in the Denki Shimbun dated September 17, 2008.

Fig. 3-16 "Ogachi Experiment Station" of
"Central Research Institute of Electric Power"

Regarding this experiment, which is a joint research between "Denchu Lab" (Central Research Institute of Electric Power Industry) and "RITE" (Technical Research Organization of Global Environment Industry), the author only suspected the danger after receiving an e-mail. This is the same risk as the experiment conducted by "RITE" in Fukazawa, Nagaoka City.

Newspaper articles disappeared from the site, so lets first introduce the news from "Electric Newspaper".

From "Electrical Newspaper" dated September 17, 2008

CO2 underground fixation, Denchu Laboratory in Akita experiment-injected into 1000m underground rock

In September, a basic experiment was conducted to inject "carbon dioxide" (CO2) dissolved in fresh water into the basement "1000 meters" and to "fix" it by reacting with the rock. On the 16th, it started at the "Ogachi Experiment Station" (Yuzawa City, Akita Prefecture) of the Central Research Institute of Electric Power.

"Carbonated water" is pushed into the cracks of the "high temperature bedrock" at about 230 degrees, and the "carbon" is "individualized" and applied to the technology development to keep it forever.

If it is put to practical use, it will be possible to fill up CO_2 even in places that are not suitable for underground storage.

It will also expand the scope of "CO_2 capture and storage (CCS) technology", which is expected as a trump card for "warming measures" .

The CCS technology, which is being developed around the world, extracts CO_2 from exhaust gases such as "charcoal-fired power plants" and applies pressure to fill them underground or under the seabed.

There is no worry of leaking to the ground, and it will be possible to store "CO_2" even in places where conventional methods are not suitable for "CO_2 storage".

This basic experiment of "CO_2 underground fixation technology" will be jointly researched by "Denchu Lab" and "RITE" .

The purpose of this research is to collect data on the speed at which CO_2 "solidifies" in the ground, and to elucidate the various conditions for "solidifying" more efficiently and quickly. .

In the experiment, 4 tons of "carbonated water" (CO_2 concentration 1%) is injected per day in a well dug down to "1000 meters" in the ground. Fresh water is injected from above, and the "water pressure" is used to push "carbonated water" into the cracks in the bedrock.

Inject every day (4 days) until 19th and measure the rate at which carbonated water enters the crack. Crystal grains of "calcium carbonate" are also placed in the same ground.

Experiments with varying "carbonated water concentration", "ground temperature" and " fresh water pressure", and collects data on the rate at which crystals grow.

Dr. Hideshi Kaieda, Senior Researcher at the Electrotechnical Research Institute of Earth Engineering, who organizes experiments, said, "If it can be put to practical use, it will increase the number of suitable sites for CO_2 storage. It is possible to push it in. "

The "Ogachi Experiment Station" is a place where "Denchu-ken" was experimenting with a new type of "geothermal power generation" technology called "high temperature rock power generation" .

From the ground, "fresh water" was pushed into the underground "1000 meters" and the "heat" was used to extract "warm water" and "steam" of 160 degrees.

Since the experiment on "Hot rock power generation" has already been completed, the experiment on "CO_2 underground storage" was started in 2002 using the well.

Since fiscal 2006, the subsidy from the Ministry of Economy, Trade and Industry has been working on "CO_2 underground fixation technology" experiments until the end of 2008.

That's it for the "Electric Newspaper" article.

*

The "CCS Experiment" has been conducted at the same place since 2002, four days before. Furthermore, since 1986, experiments on "hot rock formation power generation" have been conducted.

Looking at the "Science Channel Video" (currently not available), they are sending "500 liters per minute" of "water" in the "Hot Rock Formation" experiment. In this experiment, they have obtained basic data on "geothermal power generation" .

In this experiment, the same "hydraulic fracturing" used in "shale gas mining" is used.

Cracks were created in the "hot heat bedrock" using the "hydraulic crushing method" , water was sent from the "press-in well" to that space (16 Tokyo Domes), and "high-heated water" from the other "suction well" . Is taken out and used for "power generation".

In principle, since water is circulated, groundwater is not pushed out like "CCS".

However, as you can see from the video, the "water recovery" is "25-30%" (initially "14%"). This means that 70 to 75% of the "water" of the total amount of injected 10,000 tons (which may be water used for "hydraulic fracturing") passes through the cracks. Will be pushed out.

By the way, the amount of CO_2 stored at the Iwanohara Experiment Station in Fukazawa, Nagaoka was 10,000 tons.

*

Also, the " joint structure" of the "rock" exposed on the ground surface is "20 degrees down north" , and in the result of the boring, the same "natural crack / fracture part" is formed underground.

The "crack" is likely to spread along the "joint" by "hydraulic fracturing" , so "water" is pushed toward the hypocenter of the "Iwate-Miyagi inland earthquake" located about 27 km east-northeast. It is quite possible that the "dissociation layer" was disturbed.

The "Ogati Experiment Station" is located along the "Kosugiyama Road" between "Akinomiya Onsen" and "Doroyu Onsen".The positional relationship with the "seismic epicenter" is as shown in the following Fig. 3-17.

Looking at the relationship between "earthquakes" and "volcanic activity" in the vicinity, a "swarm earthquake" has occurred in the vicinity of the experimental site since 2007 at "Akinomiya Onsen / Takamatsudake". The connection with the "CCS experiment" started in 2002 is suspected.

The "CCS Experiment" (4 days) reported by "Electric Newspaper" does not "circulate" "water" like "high-temperature rock power generation".

The purpose is to store "water" containing "CO2" underground and "fix" it. So, the "water" pushed out by the " automatically   method " should move to the "high temperature zone" and make the "water dissociation state" unstable.

The amount of "water" to be "pressed in" is a small amount of "4 tons per

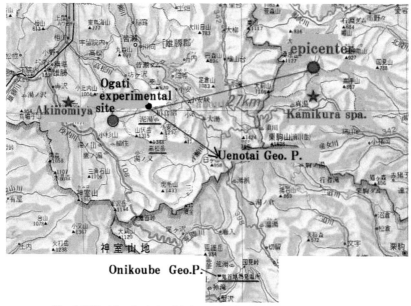

Fig. 3-17 Positional relationship between "Ogati Experimental Site" and
"seismic epicenter" of "Iwate-Miyagi Inland Earthquake"

day" , but the "fresh water amount" flowing from the top is unknown.

Since the experiment was a short period of "4 days" , it was thought that "there is little possibility of disturbing the dissociation layer" , but in fact, since September 17, 2009, a "swarm earthquake" has occurred in the vicinity. .

It is clear that "earthquakes" will occur even in the short-term "CCS experiment" .

Fig. 3-18 "CCS experiment" (only 4 days) caused "swarm earthquake" from the next day

Therefore, it can be said that the "CCS experiment" started in 2002 is likely to be the cause of the "2008 Iwate-Miyagi inland earthquake" .

The previous experiment was also "hydraulic crushing" , so it cannot be said that it has no relation.

While the cause of the "earthquake" has not been fully elucidated, it should be recognized that it is extremely dangerous to blindly understand the "fault earthquake theory" and to add artificial manipulation to the "underground environment" .

*

Although it is not as dangerous as the "CCS experiment" , the "high-temperature rocky zone power generation experiment" for "geothermal power generation" was conducted in 1986, and the relationship with the "Iwate-Miyagi inland earthquake" was also investigated. need to do it.

In fact, in 1998, the "sizukuisi earthquake (Iwate Prefecture)" occurred near two "geothermal power plants" of "Matsukawa" and "Cacconda" .

In addition, behind the "Sumikawa Onsen (Akita Prefecture)" , there is also a "landslide" that spans 400m wide and 700m long.

The "Iwate-Miyagi Inland Earthquake" recorded a largacceleration of 4000 gal. Judging from the "large collapse" that occurred upstream of the

"Aratozawa Dam" , we think that the probability of an "artificial explosion earthquake" is high.

*

The contents of the "CCS Experiment" since 2002 are unclear, but the commentary in the video states that "10,000 tons of water was added for crushing".

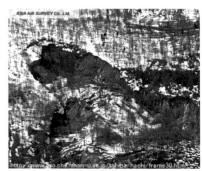

Fig. 3-19 "Slide" in the back of
"Sumikawa Onsen"

This is the same capacity as the "injection amount" of "liquefied CO_2" conducted in "Nagaoka".

The distance from the "press-in site" to the "seismic epicenter" is also in the range of "20-30 km".

If the "Chuetsu earthquake" is an "artificial earthquake" , the "Iwate-Miyagi inland earthquake" can also be an "artificial earthquake" .

Even "Denver" in Colorado, where "hot rocks" are deep underground, it has been proven that "earthquakes" can occur if "waste liquid" is injected.

In this area, there is a "hot heat bedrock" in a shallow basement, and there are several "hot springs" around it. Sending "fluid" to the basement in such a place may further increase the "probability of an earthquake".

The "earthquake" that was suspected to be caused by "liquid injection" into the ground by "CCS" continued, but finally, on March 11, 2011, the "Great East Japan Earthquake" Has happened.

The "tsunami" that hit the "Fukushima Daiichi Nuclear Power Station" is known to have hit both the "South" and the "North" . The "big tsunami" that hit from the "south" could be the "earthquake tunami" caused by "CCS" . At that time, CCS was conducted off the coast of Iwaki.

This major issue is discussed in detail in Chapter 6 as the "Unknown

Truth of the Great East Japan Earthquake".

[3-7] "Earthquake" associated with "shale gas mining"

In "shale gas mining", there is a problem that environmental destruction occurs due to the treatment of "waste liquid" used in "hydraulic fracturing".

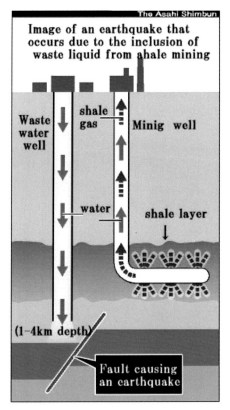

Fig. 3-20 Explanation of "shale gas mining" and "waste liquid injection"

In the homes of local residents, an outrageous thing such as "burning water from the tap" is happening.

However, there are two serious problems other than "environmental destruction".

① Expansion of earthquake scale

Since the "Earthquake in Denver", it has been confirmed that an earthquake occurs when liquid is injected into the ground. However, the fundamental problem is that due to the mistake of "Seismology", it is only possible to understand that the fault has become slippery due to liquid injection.

In the United States, since it is being carried out at a location far from the "volcanic belt", only "small earthquakes" have occurred, but if "earthquakes" occur frequently, it is possible that "magma will rise".

In the future, there is a risk of a "large earthquake" .

② Potential for continental changes

In order to "mine" "shale gas" , "hydraulic crushing" using "chemical solution" is performed to change "hard rock" called "shale" into "fragile rock" .

I am worried that this will lead to a major change in the crust in the future.

As suggested by the "Arkansas earthquake", even if it is in the continent, if the study of "seismic hydrogen implosion theory" is not advanced rapidly, it may physically sink.

[3-8] Other "earthquake occurrence" examples

In addition, an "earthquake" may occur at the dam site.

The "Hoover Dam earthquake" in the United States is famous, but it is also happening in "Japan".

The occurrence of the "Sichuan Great Earthquake" in China is not unrelated to "the construction of many " dams " around the epicenter" .

"Sichuan Province" is a base for "nuclear weapon production" in China, and a large-scale "hydroelectric power plant" has been built to secure energy.

When the "water depth of the reservoir" exceeds "100 meters", the "water dissociation conditions" in the deep underground are changed by the "water pressure". This causes "chemical destabilization of the dissociation layer" and may cause "earthquake".

There are many "earthquake occurrence examples" in "India" and "Egypt", etc., but "earthquakes" do not occur in the "Himalayan mountainous areas" even if "water storage depth" increases.

This may be because the magma is only in the deep part because the crust is thick in the "Himalayan hinterland".

From the knowledge of "Hydrogen Implosion" , it is natural that "risk" increases when the "water storage depth" changes drastically.

The risk of "earthquake occurrence" increases when the "storage depth" changes on a daily basis, such as "pumped storage power generation" .

In order to minimize changes in "large dams" as much as possible, it is necessary to keep "water level control" in a state close to "natural lakes" .

Chapter 4

Evidence that the earthquake is implosion

We have already written a lot of evidence
that "earthquakes" are "implosion phenomena".
The following are specific examples.

In particular, I would like construction engineers
to understand that "architectural brackets"
are damaged by the occurrence of "large accelerations"
that were unforeseen.
I would also like politicians and media officials
to know that this "unexpected acceleration"
is not unrelated to "CCS work".

[4-1] "Jumping stone" phenomenon

When the "vertical acceleration" due to an earthquake exceeds "980 gal", stones on the ground jump into the air.

There is a story that "Furniture and TV flew in the house." In addition, there is a story of an old man who said that a "gravestone" or "upper part of the lantern" flew and the dead appeared.

In the "Chuetsu Earthquake," some people witnessed that "the radish in the field had jumped and jumped. It seemed that white rabbits were jumping and playing."

Even if the fault moves suddenly, the radish will not escape into the air.

[4-2] "Building hardware" (Holdan) damaged

In the article (June 2005) of the architect "Hideo Uno", there was a case where "Holdan metal fittings" were damaged by the "Chuetsu earthquake".

He expressed his sincere desire to clarify this matter scientifically.

http://homepage3.nifty.com/net-forum/honnne/honnelink/20050602.htm

"Holdan metal fittings" are rugged fittings that are embedded in concrete foundations and connect "wooden house pillars" and "foundations" — that is, "seat belts" in "wooden houses" It seems to be.

It seemed impossible to imagine that it would "break" due to an "earthquake" . In the article, he states:

Originally, the "country" , "wood housing center" , or "academic society" is the main issue that should be investigated.

So, unless we recognize that an "earthquake" is an "implosion phenomenon," we cannot explain the destruction of the "Holdan metal fittings" .

Fig. 4-1 "Holdan metal "

Description of "Uno" – threats over "2500 gal" . Longing for scientific clarification! !

Everyone. Do you know what this photo is?

Fig. 4-2 "Holdan metal fittings"

This is a sad figure of "Holdan hardware" that was hurt by the direct earthquake in Niigata Chuetsu last year.

I think this is a precious photograph that remains in history.

There is a "nut" in the center. A small object is caught in the "nut" . This is the "bolt wreckage".

Most people didn't trust me even though they said that the "Holdan hardware" was cut off in a direct earthquake. "That idiot ..."

But if you look at this picture, you can trust that I'm not a big fan.

Write the same thing over and over again.

The seismic intensity meter at the Kawaguchi Town Hall had a "Seismic intensity" of "7" and "Gal" exceeded "2500".

"Gal" was incredible, "three times" the "Hanshin Awaji Earthquake" . And the "house collapse rate" around the town hall was around "30%" .

*

I was really disappointed when I participated in the presentation of "Chuetsu Earthquake Damage Report Meeting" jointly held by 7 academic societies.

In other words, no one is approaching the actual situation of the threat of "2500 gal" or more, "I see the trees and not the forest".

In this situation, the valuable records and materials brought about by the incredible "quake" will remain "dead". Nothing will be passed on to future generations as a valuable asset for mankind.

Is it okay to have such a stupid thing?

*

I am eager to see a new move from this picture.

This is the disappointment and anger of Mr. Uno.

The "Chuetsu offshore earthquake" occurred after the "Chuetsu earthquake". The "Iwate-Miyagi Inland Earthquake" actually recorded an impact exceeding "4,000 gal".

However, there is still a misguided argument such as There must have been an " undiscovered active fault ".

How do seismologists explain the "destruction" of this "Holdan hardware" ?

The "building industry" has also lost the chance to recognize that "earthquake" is "implosion detonation".

Also, an article from December 2004 complains that the safety myth of "Holdan" is broken.

At the time of the Great Hanshin Earthquake, a "thin pillar wooden structure" that does not have a "seat belt" called "Holdan metal fittings" was removed from the foundation on one side due to "swing" . Immediately after that, there was a tragedy in which the central pillar collapsed and "5000 people" were immediately crushed.

For this reason, the use of "Holdan hardware" has become commonplace, and "base" and "pillar" do not rise.

If you embed "Holdan", you cannot destroy it. Most people, not just me, believed in the myth.

In the "Holdan hardware" certified by Timber House Technology Center, the thick "anchor" was broken even though the "screw" or "drawer hardware" was not removed.

And the "post hardware" that can withstand small loads just to support the house broke.

Do earthquakes with a seismic intensity of 7 have more power than expected?

Or was this area more than seismic intensity 7?

Anyway, there are a lot of facts that architects can't handle.

The "instantaneous phenomenon" of "destruction of metal fittings" cannot be explained without realizing that the "earthquake" is an "implosion phenomenon" .

This is an important finding for those in the world of engineering, but for seismologists it is a kind of OOPART(out-of-place-artifacts). With this, there is no progress.

*

In addition, "the act of injecting a liquid object" into several kilometers of the ground artificially causes "implosion" in a place of about 10 kilometer—that is, sometimes "shock damage" that is larger than a natural earthquake. We must recognize early on that there is a risk of it happening.

[4-3] "Sea earthquake phenomenon" and "boat capsize"

The 2007 Noto-oki earthquake occurred in Toyama Bay, and there was news that "boat capsizing" .

As a testimony of the victims, "Jiji Press" said that "there were two earthquakes" . Here, we introduce articles from the Asahi Shimbun.

Damage in Toyama and Niigata "Liquefaction" and "Boat overturning" Noto-oki earthquake
March 25, 2007

In Toyama Prefecture, where a seismic intensity of less than 5 was recorded, there were damages such as "boat overturning" and "liquefaction phenomenon at the port" , which are thought to be caused by "sea level change" .

Around 11:40 am on Toyama Bay, about 1.1 km off the coast of Mizuhashi fishing port in Toyama City, a patrol boat from the Fushiki Coast Guard rescued the men. The four men, including the male captain, were held on the hull of an overturned "pleasure boat" (approximately 6.3m long). The men were residents of Toyama Prefecture and all were not injured.
Fushiki Coast Guard believes that it may have been overturned due to "sea level change" due to "earthquake" .

According to Fushiki Coast Guard, the four were fishing from early in the morning, and the captain said, "At around 9:42 am The boat turned upside-down with a banging vibration. "

According to the Toyama Regional Meteorological Observatory, the "tide level fluctuation" 7 cm above and below was observed in "Toyama Bay" shortly after the "earthquake" .

This is a phenomenon called "sea shock" or "sea earthquake" that occurs where the "push cone" intersects the ocean floor.

The author's "solving the mystery of earthquakes" includes incorrect drawings of "refraction relations" , so here are the corrected drawings.

Since "seismic waves" move from "rock", which has a high wave propagation speed, to "in the sea" where the propagation speed is slow, energy concentrates on the ship floating on the sea as shown in the figure.

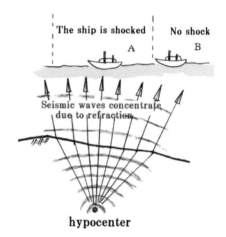

Fig. 4-3 Sea earthquake
(earthquake refraction phenomenon)

It gives a strong impact. In this case, it was overturned because it was a small "pleasure boat".

In the case of a large ship, it will shake greatly. The captain wonders if he has boarded a "reef" that is not on the chart or has collided with a "submarine" . The captain hurries up and examines the hull, but usually keeps sailing because there is no damage.

This "sea shock" phenomenon has long been known as a mysterious phenomenon that occurs only in a region where "seismic energy" is concentrated, and that a "ship" passing through a slightly distant route does not feel anything.

This is powerful evidence that tells us that an "earthquake" is an "explosion phenomenon" .

In the 1995 Great Hanshin-Awaji Earthquake, we received an e-mail with the following experiences from those who boarded the "Ferry" from "Oita to Kobe via Matsuyama" on the day of the earthquake.

In fact, at that time of the Great Hanshin-Awaji Earthquake, I was on the "Ferry" from "Oita departure to Kobe via Matsuyama".

Just when I passed the Akashi Strait, I encountered an earthquake.
It is one of the few people who experienced "that earthquake" at "above" of "the epicenter" and "at sea".

I stayed up late at night, but when I was asleep, I was suddenly hit by the sound of "Don !!!!" I woke up.
There are many shallows in Setouchi, so I thought, "Did you stranded?", But the ship was moving, so I thought strangely, I left the sleeper room and went to the lobby.
When I looked at other customers, they all seemed to have a mysterious face, "What was it?"

There is no "rolling" or "pitching". There was no "tsunami" just because there was a "sound" and "shock" that struck "don!" Just once.
I had been wondering for a long time that it would be such a shock if the "fault" suddenly shifted.

I saw your site and thought, "Ah! That ' s it!"
Certainly, the impact is similar to the "explosion impact".
In addition, because the transportation was paralyzed, after the "earthquake," it was canned 24 hours at sea, but the "aftershock shake" has never been experienced.

Combining these, the consensus goes to the theory that "earthquake is an implosion phenomenon" advocated at your site.".

[4-4] Debris flow and yamatsunami

The "largest earthquake area" in the "1923 Great Kanto Earthquake" is "under Kanagawa Prefecture", which is often hidden behind the misery of the "Great Fire Damage in Tokyo".
"Village of mountain landslide" appears in "Tanzawa area" and "Southern Hakone" in Kanagawa Prefecture.

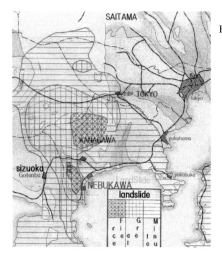

Fig. 4-4 Distribution of damage in Nebukawa
that was attacked by the yamatsunami

Fig. 4-5 "Yamatsunami Disaster(mud avalanche)"
in "Nebugawa"

"Tokyo" and "Yokohama" were severely damaged by "fire" , but in terms of "earthquake," a tragic event happened in which one village disappeared.

In particular, the "disaster case of the entire train" caused by the "Yamatsunami" that occurred in the "Nebugawa" must be recognized as a phenomenon associated with "implosion detonation" , which is different from a simple "collapse" .

The report from the Taisho Earthquake Journal reports

The southern part of Odawara (Kanagawa Prefecture), about 1.5 miles (6 km) from Kataura, was hit by a tsunami following the earthquake. "Kataura Village" along the Atami Railway was hit by "Yamatsunami" due to the landslide.

A part of "Sixty House" was buried in the basement more than 30m. Excavation is impossible.
In addition, the train from Tokyo to Manazuru, which was stopped at Negawa Station, was swallowed by Yamatsunami in addition to the stop where about 200 passengers ride. Surrounded by earth and sand, sinking deep into the sea, the "living spirit" had to float forever as a ghost of the Sagami clan.

Another section includes the following explanations:

"Nebugawa" is one of the most devastating things in the prefecture (Kanagawa) due to the destruction of mountains.

Before the earthquake, the "nebu River" was about 3.6 m wide and the river mouth that poured into the sea was a bay. There was a small village where about 30 houses were counted.

The "Nebugawa Railway Bridge" was built on this village and was a large bridge with a length of 90 m and a height of 30 m.

However, the upper mountain of about one and a half miles (6km) collapsed due to the earthquake, and a tsunami (in Japanese named Yamatunami) occurred. The mountain tsunami pushed the fallen tree earth and sand toward the coast, and the trees on the riverbank were buried deeply and stopped the traces, and the entire part of the above mentioned part was buried in just 5 minutes. Or pushed it into the sea.
As a result, the number of dead residents has reached 80 or so.

The stubborn iron bridge was destroyed, and one train that was stopped at the stop was washed away with the passengers in the sea. A great disaster occurred.

The village "Yonegami" was in a similar state, and about half of the villages, "Thirty Houses" were buried due to "Yamatsunami" , and more than 50 people died. "

The "slope collapse" of the mountain caused by the "earthquake disaster" does not seem to have the power to "destroy" the "solid iron bridge" by flowing down "6 kilometers" .

"Yamatsunami (in Japanese)" generated by a "Great Earthquake" is a phenomenon called "powder flow" or "debris flow" in which "gas erupting from the underground" carries "sediment" .

When the "Nagano-ken Seibu Earthquake" occurred, "Yamatunami" that occurred from the middle of the west slope of "Ontake Mountain" caused great damage to the downstream "Otaki Village" .

This was also a mountain tsunami, where "explosive gas" transports earth and sand and flows down at high speed.

*

At larger scales, it becomes like the "mountain collapse phenomenon" of "Mount St. Helens" or "Mount Bandai" .

An incident similar to the tragedy of Nebukawa has become a "drama" by "Okamoto Kidou" as "Nadati's collapse" .
"Nadati" is a village that faces the Sea of Japan and is near "Kasugayama" , the residence of Kenshin Uesugi.

[4-5] Sinking of Uryuu Island (horizontal explosion (energy release))

The story of "Uryuu Island Sinking" is an actual island in "Beppu Bay (Oita Prefecture)" that appeared in "Newton" (1991Vol.11No9) as the "Atlantis Story" of Japan.
However, it is recognized as "just a legend" in current science and scientifically impossible. It has been confirmed by hydrogen implosion.

Fig. 4-6 Uryuu Island crowded with foreign ships entering the port (Newton Vol.11, No.9)

According to the commentary of "Newton Magazine" , "Uryuu Island" prospered as a "port town of a foreign ship" during the Sengoku period and sank into "Beppu Bay" overnight due to an "earthquake" . If you look at the old map, you can see the names of "Minami-honmachi" , "Naka-honmachi" , "Kitaura-machi" etc.

According to the book "Houhu-Monjyo", the sinking situation is as follows.

"Uryujima" faces the "Hunai Sea" and is a large port town that is crowded day and night by boat throughout Japan. This island was about 3-5km from "Hunai Town" and about 2.2km off-shore from current "Oita City Shukugocho".

In the first year of Keicho, at 2:00 pm on July 12, the land was torn and a landslide occurred. However, it stopped after a while.

When the residents were finally relieved, the sea began to "ring", and people fled in all directions and evacuated to the mountains and fields. Even in the city of Hunai, people who feared drowning gathered in the "Seiya town" on the hill.

At this time, the water in the wells of the villages suddenly dried up, and after a while, "mountainous water swelled on the surface of the sea, and it came to the city.
Sea water overflowed in "Hunai" and its "villages in the vicinity", and the houses were washed away.
Six hours later, after the water was finally drained, most of the large and small houses in Hunai collapsed, and there were numerous deaths of humans.
"Uryuu Island" disappeared without a trace and sank to the seabed.

The above is the "sinking situation".
Like "Atlantis", it disappeared into the sea in a catastrophic night.

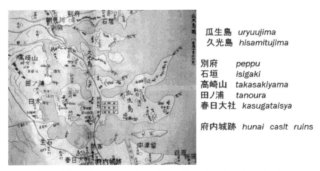

Fig. 4-7 Old map of "Uryuu Island" and "Hisamitu Island"

Fig. 4-7 is drawn in the "Hoyo Ancient Story" at the end of the Edo period.
The "place name" in the figure, and the "village name" and "shrine" on

the current map are written in "red". You can see that it remains quite.

"Hunai" is the name of the place where the castle was located, and it seems to be called "Hunai Castle". Shown in blue.

According to Professor Kazuhiko Hamano's book, "Uryuu Island consists of two islands, 12 villages, and more than 1,000 residents".

Looking at the map, the story seems quite reliable.

"Two islands" will be "Uryuu island" and "Hisamitu island".

In addition, some uninhabited islands have disappeared.

Geophysics does not accept historical events with this clear material. It is an arrogance of a geophysicist to conclude that "the island cannot sink, according to the latest theory in geophysics" and "Uryuu island sinking is a fictional story that is only a legend".

It's just a theory that is wrong and should not be taken.

*

The story of "Uryuu Island Sinking" is also a powerful proof of "Hydrogen Implosion".

Since the "explosion direction" was "horizontal", Uryuu Island is considered to have entered the "pull area" and "sunk."

When "Sonic Profiling" is performed in "Beppu Bay", you can see the fault that the "Oita" side is greatly displaced.

It can also be seen that the "sea floor" has become quite "flat" due to "sediment" over the years.

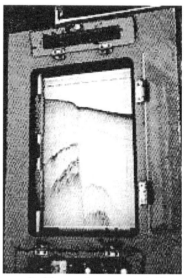

Fig. 4-8 The result of the sound wave survey in Beppu Bay proves that there is a clear level difference.

Chapter 5

Contradiction of Active Fault Theory

The author also wrote the reason for urgent publication
of this book in "Preface".
That is because the "Nuclear Regulatory Commission"
is trying to twist the important productions of the nation
with the meaningless theory of active faults.
Knowing that a fault can be caused by a major earthquake,
only "existing faults" are inspected.
So why can we make the "world's safest installation standards"?

[5-1] Contradiction of "active fault"

In the explanation so far, you may have understood that "active fault theory" is wrong.

An "active fault" is a "scratch" that occurs as a result of "hydrogen implosion detonation".

Therefore, no matter how closely we examine these "scratches," we cannot know when the "earthquake recurrence" will occur.

The author appeals to the "Nuclear Regulatory Commission" to hear the opinions of "Implosive Seismo Detonation".

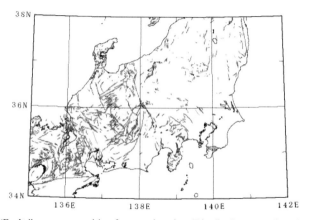

Fig. 5-1 "Faults" are scars resulting from earthquakes (Distribution map of "active faults")

Fig. 5-1 shows data for "active faults" by the "Active Fault Study Group".

Since the "fault" has a large area, the total of the "fault surface" in this way exceeds "the whole land area of Japan" .

Dr. Satosi Asada is famous as "the first person in seismology" . He raised this issue by writing a paper titled "The Problem of Class C Active Faults" seven years before his death.

The following is an excerpt of the content.

"Active faults" are classified into "A" , "B" , and "C" according to "activity" .
"A" is the most active, with a frequency of once every 1000 years, B once every 10,000 years, and C once every 100,000 years.
"C class" is 10 times (7000) of "B class" (about 700).
Adding the "seismic region" of "C class fault" , it becomes "20 times" the land area of Japan. Obviously something is wrong because this is not possible.
Where is the problem?

This is the question raised by Dr. Asada.

This time, the "Nuclear Regulatory Commission" jumped over the frequency of 100,000 years to "400,000 years", so the question of "Dr. Asada" becomes even bigger.

The answer as "Implosive Seismo Detonation" to this problem has been explained so far.

"Earthquake" is not caused by "movement of a fault" .
"Hydrogen implosion" is an "earthquake" , and "fault" is a "crustal displacement" that appears only in the case of a "large earthquake" . "Faults" do not appear in "small earthquakes" .
Even if there is no "fault" , a "fault" may appear if a "giant earthquake" occurs.
It is clear from the fact that "fault" appeared after "earthquake" at the "nuclear power plant base" that was investigated in detail.
For example, Kashiwazaki Kariwa Nuclear Power Station.

[5-2] Meaning of "fault" found after "earthquake"

As with the "Kashiwazaki Kariwa nuclear power plant" that suffered damage from the "Chuetsu offshre earthquake", "faults" are often found after large earthquake.

In the "Fukuoka earthquake", the Kego fault, which had been confirmed only in the land area, had been extended to the "sea area" because the investigation was insufficient.

Professor Tokihiko Matsuda, Professor Emeritus of the University of Tokyo says,

I once participated in the "Kego Fault" survey, but when I looked at "Hakata Bay" , it did not show that the fault continued into the sea.

There are technical barriers to the coastal survey, which may not have been found in a limited period of time.

However, it is highly possible that the "fault" did not exist from the beginning.

In the "Noubi earthquake (Gihu)", a "fault" suddenly appeared in a field that had no faults.

According to the farmer's witness, "Some time after the earthquake, it slipped and became a large fault" .

According to the "current theory" , there are "seismic faults that are actively moving even if they do not appear on the surface of the earth" or there are "hidden faults" deeply.

However, this is difficult to understand mechanically.

It is well known that even if there is a major damage on the "surface" , there will be no damage in the "coal mine" deep underground.

This is because the "ground surface" is a "free end" in terms of "dynamic theory" and moves well.

Deep parts like coal mines are hard to move at the "restraint end".

Therefore, "moving only near the hypocenter, which is the constraining end" , is difficult to understand for those who have learned "dynamic mechanics" .

The concept of "Hypocenter Fault" is a "belief" that started with active fault theory.

What happens at "hypocenter" is "implosion", not the first discrepancy. "Slip phenomenon" such as "Landslide" occurs only at the "free end" where it is not restrained.

Now, if a new fault may occur after an earthquake, no matter how rigorously the "active fault survey" is, it would be meaningless.

The "Nuclear Regulatory Commission" says "to create the safest standards in the world" , but the "earthquake" occurs where there is no "fault" , and the possibility of a new "fault" is recognized. If so, there is a logical contradiction in itself based on the existence of "active faults".

Does the committee member not notice this contradiction?

[5-3] How can the "first fault" be created?

"Professor Yasuhiro Umeda" of "Disaster Prevention Research Institute, Kyoto University" wrote in the "Disaster Prevention Research Newsletter" entitled "Problems struck by the 2000 Western Tottori Earthquake" .

> With regard to this "earthquake," we received a number of questions from media-related people: "Why did an earthquake occur in a place without an active fault?"
> Since the "Hyogoken-Nanbu Earthquake" , it seems that many people have heard that "an earthquake occurs in an " active layer " , but that is not true.
> "Earthquake" is a phenomenon in which the crustal rock mass shifts rapidly, and the result of the shift is a "fault" . Therefore, even if there is no "fault" in advance, the "first earthquake" may occur.
> As a result, the "first fault" is formed in the "crust" .
> The "fault" does not always appear on the "surface" from the beginning.
> Many earthquakes occurred on the same fault, and the gaps piled up so that the surface could finally be revealed. It is recognized as an active fault by the eyes of geologists.
> This "earthquake" made me recognize the relationship between "earthquake" and "active fault" again.

Then, it must be able to explain what causes the "first fault". The "Nuclear Regulation Committee" "Seismologist" who wants to regulate only the "Earthquake" from the "second time" must face the contradiction honestly.

*

The same "logical contradiction" can be said for "active movement theory of plates" .

The mechanism of plate movement is explained as "the table cloth falls down by the " self-weight " of the plate itself that has become heavier and sinks".

If so, followers of plate theory must explain how the first plate moves.

If there is no explanation for "first fault" or "first plate", it must be said that logic is poor.

[5-4] From Dr. Kunihiko Shimazaki's "The true nature of the earthquake "

"The Vice-Chairman Shimazaki" of the "Nuclear Regulatory Commission" stated in the book "The Reality of Earthquakes" as follows:

"Earthquake" is something that occurs in the "seismic region" , and as a result, "earthquake waves" are generated. It is a phenomenon that shakes the "earth" and shakes "buildings". (Omitted)

It was only about thirty years ago that the "seismic wave" in the "seismic region" , the "true nature of namazu" , was discovered.
There have been various controversies over the past decades, and at one time there was even a "seismic source = black box theory" .
We don't know what is happening in the "earthquake area" , so we don't think about the cause and we are going to study the waves generated by the earthquake.

The conclusion of the controversy came from the paper of "Takuo Maruyama" (who retired from the Tsukuba Earthquake Research Institute several years ago).
It is still an achievement when he was a graduate student.

In the "seismic region" , the mass block slides on a specific plane (called the "fault surface"), and the slide generates "seismic waves" . (Omitted)

As a result, a "fault" is created at the "fault surface" . For this reason, this type of displacement motion that creates faults is called fault motion.

Of course, if there is a fault already, the displacement of the fault becomes even larger.
It can be said that this is the "catfwish true nature" because faulting creates earthquake waves.

[5-5] "Proof assuming existence from the beginning" does not become "true proof"

"Maruyama' s paper" means "double couple proved".

According to the explanation by Dr. Shimazaki, "Earthquake phenomenon" means that "something" occurs in "hypocenter", resulting in "earthquake waves".
The "something" here may be "hydrogen implosion".

However, in the latter half, he concludes that the mass is shifted from a certain plane (fault plane), and that the movement causes a "earthquake".
Obviously, from the beginning, the "argument" is underway, assuming that "the fault exists".

Even if you think that "faults are generated by " hydrogen implosion ", it should be no problem." Therefore, it is wrong to determine that the fault motion is the true nature of the earthquake.
At the time of introducing a "surface" (fault surface), the proof is not already valid.

"Dr. Ishimoto" argued against "fault theorists" who claimed that "fault theory" was proved from "initial motion distribution".

They initially assumed that the hypocenter was a fault in the "hypocenter" and decided that it was the "cause of the earthquake" because the initial distribution was not against that assumption.
This is not a "correct proof" from a logical point of view because the "claim to be concluded" is already included in the "premise".
In other words, even if it is assumed that "earthquake radiation" is not "fault formation", if the "initial distribution" is explained, the above claims will be immediately This is because it will fail.

He stated above.

*

As explained at the beginning of this book, "generation of fault" can be explained by "equilibrium failure explosion" (Energy release) mainly due to Implosion Detonation is. Therefore, it cannot be said that the proof that "the active fault is the cause of the earthquake" has been established.

*

Since "Shinkai 6500" denied "Plate theory", it was not really necessary to mention this in this chapter.

However, it seems that "active fault theory" is "truth" and is taught in school education. Therefore, it seems to be tedious, but repeatedly explained "the consequence of Implosive Seismo Detonation".

Chapter 6

The Unknown Truth of the Great East Japan Earthquake

The truth of the Great East Japan Earthquake
has yet to be elucidated.
Why did such a "giant tsunami" hit the Tohoku coast?
We have to urgently investigate, but even the prestigious
organization of tsunami engineering does not grasp this truth.

[6-1] The truth of the tsunami that hit Tohoku

http://nationalgeographic.jp/nng/article/20120215/299297/

As shown above URL, the tsunami that hit the Tohoku coast was an "overlapping phenomenon". It is recognized that the first tsunami ① overlaps with the "second tsunami ②", which has a sharp peak shown in Fig. 6-1, causing major damage.

And the cause of this "second tsunami" is interpreted as "branch fault" near the trench axis and "this may have occurred by jumping up".

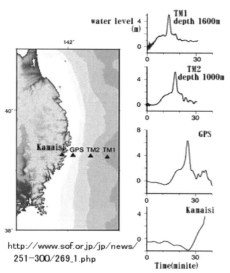

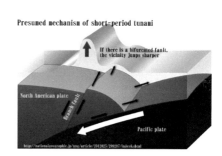

Fig. 6-2 In the current thory, the jumping of the branch fault is considered to be the cause of the short-period tunami.

Fig. 6-1 Record of "3.11 earthquake tsunami" by tsunami meter installed off Kamaishi. You can see that the tsunami generated by the earthquake in ② is very large.

However, in the deep sea of 1600m (TM1 University of Tokyo Earthquake Research Institute Tsunami Meter), it is unlikely that "the force to lift seawater as much as 3m" will be caused by "plate jumping".

*

The "Implosive Seismo Detonation" interprets that the second tsunami was caused by the earthquake explosion ②shown in Fig. 6-4 andFig.6-5.

In other words, we believe that the sea floor generated acceleration exceeding 4000 gal recorded in the "Iwate Miyagi Inland Earthquake".

It is interpreted as a tsunami caused by a small-scale submarine explosion.

The "Tunami meter" installed at the port between "Soma" and "Hatinohe" has been destroyed, but the cause is due to this "short cycle" giant tsunami (tsunami caused by the earthquake in ②).

In other words, the truth can be said to be a "complex tsunami" in which "tsunami of ②" overlaps with "tsunami of ①" as shown in Figure 6-4.

In the earthquake of ②, a "large collapse – landslide" occurred on the seabed.

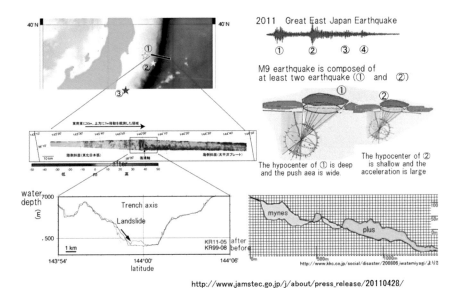

http://www.jamstec.go.jp/j/about/press_release/20110428/

Fig.6-3 The truth of the tsunami that hit the Tohoku coast (especially the coast of Iwate Miyagi, apart from Fukushima)

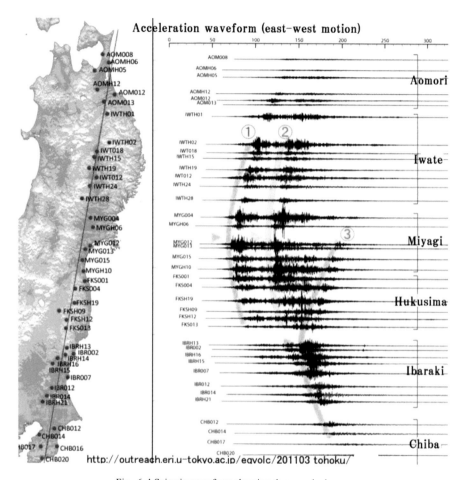

Fig. 6-4 Seismic waveform showing three explosions

It is similar to the "Large Collapse" that was prevalent in the "Northern Aratosawa Dam" during the "Iwate Miyagi Inland Earthquake" . (Fig.6-3)
However, under the "Fukushima coast" (especially the Fukushima Daiichi nuclear power plant) is another "overlap" of tsunamis.

In the following explanation, we will indicate the possibility of the

96

cause of of the earthquake tsunami③ caused by CCS (Carbon Dioxicide Capture and Storage) or natural gas mining conducted off the coast of Iwaki.

[6-2] There were at least "three explosions"

The "Great East Japan Earthquake" that occurred on March 11, 2011 is said to be a "linked earthquake".

However, it is difficult to have a physical image of the explanation that "a vast sliding surface is generated by interlocking".

In the explanation by the "current theory", "hypocenter" is said to be the " start point of destruction " where the " fault " begins to slide, and the destruction spreads along the sliding surface sequentially ".

However, this does not make a reasonable explanation for "ground deformation".

Considering the "Implosive Seismo Detonation", it can be seen that the "multiple explosions" clearly caused the damage.

The feature of the "M9 earthquake" is that at least three large explosions occurred in just 2-3 minutes, as can be seen from Figure 6-4 published by "The University of Tokyo Earthquake Research Institute".

Using the analysis method shown in Fig. 6-4, it is possible to determine to some extent where the "earthquake" occurred. This is because there is no difference in arrival time for earthquakes that occurred farther away.

Explosion of ① ... First earthquake off "Ojika Peninsula"
Explosion of ②… It occurs a little in "southeast waters" from ①
Explosion of ③… Occurring near the coast of "Iwaki City"

If you look at the amount of horizontal movement, you can see the composition of three explosions.

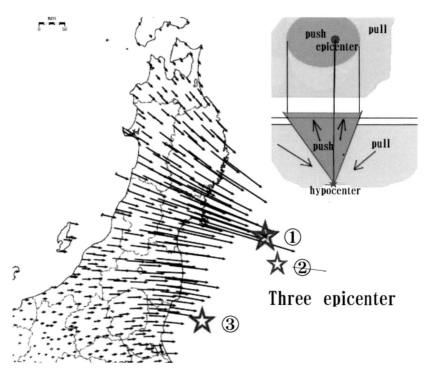

Fig. 6-5 Distribution of "horizontal movement" due to "earthquake" towards three "epicenters"

"Big explosions" have occurred three times, but all three are explosions close to " direct-under earthquakes ". So you can see all the land areas are "pull areas" , and they are moving toward their epicenters.

The current fault theory cannot grasp the relationship with these physical quantities. The problem is "Explosion ③".

"Unknown truth" about the "tsunami" that may have been caused by the "explosion of ③" that occurred off the coast of "Iwaki City Nakoso".

[6-3] "CCS Project" was underway in "Iwaki City"

In fact, the fact that a "CCS project" was being implemented at this location cannot be ignored.

As introduced in Chapter 2, we sent an e-mail to warn the project head of "RITE" that "CCS" could cause a "earthquake" .

The "damaged earthquake" in "Denver" in the United States may have been caused by "water injection" into the "underground" .
For this reason, we would like you to review the "CCS Project" in Japan.

The answer included the meaning of "I am okay because I have received the guidance of Professor Emeritus of the University of Tokyo" and the following "rejective" words.

"We ask for appropriate opinions and responses based on scientific evidence, not " speculation " from " overseas cases " in different situations. "

The reply from the author was shown in [3-5].

No matter what scholars you have, you are all natural when it comes to unknown science. Therefore, it may be that "scholars did not know at that time" . Even if the scholar's deliberation (approval) eliminates legal responsibility, moral responsibility may remain.
What I am most concerned about is that there may be a mistake in knowledge about the cause of the earthquake, which makes it easy to carry out easy human engineering deep underground. As a result, it may cause a lot of tragedy.

Above lette was sent.

*

Three years later, the Chuetsu-oki earthquake occurred, and four years later, the Iwate-Miyagi inland earthquake, and this time, the "earthquake tsunami" off Iwaki City.
The tragedy that was worried had just happened.

*

In the meantime, foolish judgments made by politicians aggravated the problem.
The international commitment under the Hatoyama Administration to

reduce CO2 emissions by 25% naturally accelerates the CCS plan.

In the "Kan administration", the "Hamaoka nuclear power plant", which had been operating without problems, was stopped with a "stop request".

The author petitioned "Chubu Electric Power Company" to disregard "Nuclear Power Plant Stop Request" by "Prime Minister Kan". There has been no request for this, and there has been a "suspension of nuclear power plant operation" in various locations, and the switch to "thermal power generation" is progressing one after another.

The "CCS plan" is becoming increasingly important and is planned for "Tomakomai" and "Kitakyushu" in the future.

The "politician's judgment" that they thought was good continues to produce great tragedy.

[6-4] "Two tsunamis" attacked "Fukushima Daiichi Nuclear Power Plant"

The reason for the problem is that the "tsunami" that occurred here may have hit the "Fukushima Daiichi Nuclear Power Plant" from "South".

For videos taken by locals,
- Tsunami came from two directions, "North" and "South"
- "Tsunami from the South" was bigger
- "Two waves" overlapped to become a "big tsunami"

Etc. have been filmed.

A field survey of "Prof. Shinji Sato" at the University of Tokyo also found that "two tsunamis" were attacked.

Details will not be described, but if you look at the records of the "tunami meter" (the instrument that measures the sea level rise and fall and "continuously records" the measurement results), tsunamis are generated in ① -② and ③ . You can see that these tsunamis overlap on the coast of Fukushima Prefecture. ①-② is tunami from the north, and ③ is tunami from the south.

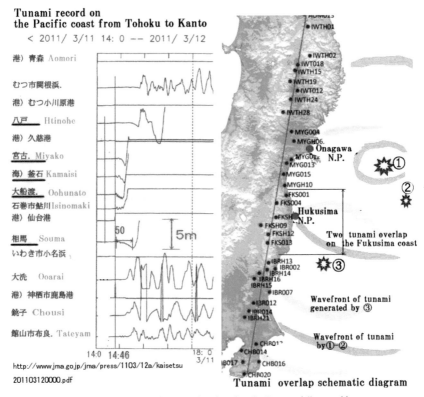

Fig. 6-6 Schematic diagram showing that the "tsunamis" caused by
"earthquake of ①-②" and "earthquake of ③" overlap.

In the southern coasts of Ibaraki and Chiba prefectures, the locations
where the two tsunami phases match and the location where they deviate
appear alternately, indicating that there is a difference in damage.

It is known that there was no "tsunami damage" in "Chiba Prefecture
Cyousi Village". If you look at the video taken from the nearby coast,
you can see that the "phase" was completely "in reverse phase".

Video of "Tsunami" that hit the beach in front of Grand Hotel "Isoya" in

"Chosi City inubouzaki"

http://www.youtube.com/watch?v=OYXqHGbi0L8

In the video above, the "mountain" of the tsunami of ①-② has arrived at the time of hitting the "valley" of the first tsunami ③ (where the tsunami of ③ arrived first).

It is filmed that the tsunami of ①-② is attacking under the condition that the rock is completely exposed to the offshore.

Even when the "mountain" of "tsunami of ①-②" arrives, the sea level is the same level as usual. It can be presumed that the same phenomenon occurred here in Chosei Village .

By the way, in the adjacent "Hasunuma Coast" and "Ichinomiya Town" , "tsunamis" entered the city and were inundated.

As can be seen from this, it is clear that at least "two tsunamis" of ①-② and ③ occurred.

And if the "tsunami of ③" did not occur, we can be sure that the "tsunami height" on the "Fukushima coast" was much smaller.

The danger of "CCS" can be assumed from the "earthquakes" caused by the recent "shale gas mining" .

In particular, in the case of "Japan" , "magma" is located in a "shallow place" . Should be careful. The author asks for it.

[6-5] Estimate when "tsunami" did not occur "off Iwaki City"

If tunami of ③ does not occur, it can be estimated that the tsunami that hit the Fukushima nuclear power was probably much smaller than the "tsunami" that hit the "Onagawa nuclear power" .

Earthquake" and "Tsunami" must be newly researched as "unknown science".

If you don't realize that you are "ignorant," there is the potential for

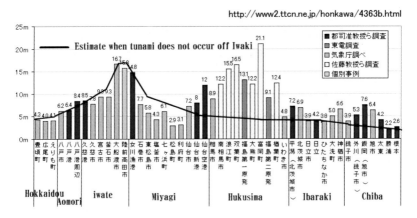

Fig. 6-7 If "Tsunami"③ did not occur, "Nuclear Power" may have been safe

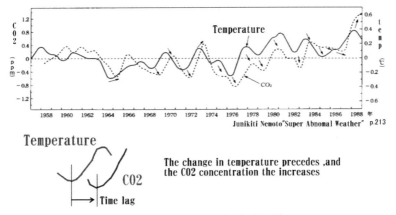

Fig.6-8 Global warming is ahead of CO2 increase

further tragedy.

Currently, the "CCS Plan" has been decided to be implemented in "Tomakomai" , but we should not be grad ro implement it.

The actual situation of "CCS" in "Iwaki City Offshore" should be investigated in more detail.

First, the leading theory is that CO2 itself is the cause of global warming. It can be understood by looking at the graph that warming first, followed by "biological activities", and it is more convincing that "CO2 increases".

Everyone must be smarter.

*

Another important thing is that "understanding of earthquake phenomena" is ambiguous.

Since the entire Tohoku Coast has subsided, "rafting work" is underway. But why did it sink? There is no "earthquake theory" that convinces the "sinking phenomenon".

Various "new concepts" have been proposed by seismologists, but they are just crazy ideas that ignore "dynamics".

- Dynamic overshooting
- Outer rise earthquake
- Asperity
- Silent earthquakes, slow earthquakes
- Hot spot
- Subduction

"Dr. Hitoshi Takeuchi" misleads young researchers in his book "How to Become a Original" as follows.

> The more "strange" the first hypothesis is, the greater progress will be made to natural science when it is demonstrated. The person who proposed that hypothesis is the "genius" in natural science.

He speaks like this, but there are people who truly take it and think, "I will be a genius in the future," and speak strange ideas.

But over time, such "ideal ideas" will disappear.

Note-1:

A feasibility study on the total system of CCS stored in a gas field off the coast of Iwaki was conducted by a NEDO project. This uses the IGCC demonstration machine in Iwaki City, Fukushima Prefecture as the source of CO2 emissions. In addition, off the coast of Nakoso and Iwaki, the Great East Japan Earthquake was triggered and the investigation was suspended for the time being.

Note-2:

Subsequent investigations revealed that the underground pressure in the "finished gas field" off Iwaki decreased from 21GPa to 5GPa. The dissociated gas generated by this pressure decrease may have caused the earthquake ③ off the coast of Iwaki. In any case, artificial alteration of the underground environment will lead to the generation of dissociated gases and create an earthquake hazard.

Chapter 7

Macroscopic anomaly mechanism

*Various phenomenon have been reported regarding the
"Macroscopic anomaly".
In "current seismology", most of them cannot be explained.
Therefore, it is almost ignored by seismologists
who support the current theory.*

*However, the "Hydrogen Implosion Seismo Theory"
can explain many phenomena scientifically.
Therefore, it is necessary to invest a budget
to replace the earthquake theory
and develop a new earthquake prediction method.
Aloso it is necessary to change the "geodetic" prediction methods
that cannot produce results such as "volumetric strain gauges"
and "GPS observations".*

[7-1] Local changes in "Geoelectric current" and "Geomagnetism"

The author's most disappointing thing is that the Takagi-type indeterminate magnetometer petition (*1, *2) for "observation network construction" was not approved at the 1974 Diet deliberation.

This deliberation was done three times, denied by seismological authorities.

---

*1:The inventor of "Magnetometer" is "Dr. Sei Takagi" of the Meteorological and Meteorological Agency.
*2: The petitioner of the deliberation is "Mr. Sadao Miyamoto" , a high school teacher.

The "existing authority" may not have been malicious, but this parliamentary deliberation has buried important knowledge about the "earthquake" .

The principle of this "earthquake prediction meter" seems to have been discovered from "wartime research" which attempted to cover the weakness of Japan, "deficiency of natural resources", by "mineral oil extraction" in the south.

Apparently, the "unpositioned magnetic system" designed to detect "electrical changes" during an "earthquake" worked surprisingly well.
"Dr. Takagi" and "Mr. Miyamoto" (a petitioner: a high school teacher) and others said, "If installed in about 200 places throughout the country, earthquake predictions can be 100% successful." It seems that he had certainty.

So they made a petition about "laying out an observation network", but seismologists at the University of Tokyo objected.
There is a review record, so you can see it, but it is far cheaper than the current "geodetic observation method" (such as "volume strain"), and the "observation network" was not completed.

If this is adopted and successful, it is clear that it will be painful for researchers on the "establishment side" who have earned enormous budgets. That's why a sly response that doesn't seem like a truth scholar will begin.

The following is a statement from Mr. Miyamoto, a petitioner.

> The highest authority in the direction of the Earth's geomagnetism recognized my idea and said, "This must be observed. It should be done. "

This is the response of seismologists.

> The principle of why "earth current" flows is unknown. Such unscientific methods cannot be adopted.

To a scholar at the University of Tokyo who opposes the "establishment of the Takagi-style observation network," a government member finally said, "It is scholars who are non-scientific…" .

> This is strange for today's scholars.
> I think that all the studies have started in the question of what the cause is and how to solve it.
> Nevertheless, "You admit the fact that it works by chance, but you don't accept the proposal because you don't know the principle of the cause of the phenomenon.
> Rather, I won't ask you questions if you haven't acknowledged the event yet. However, isn't it possible to advance your studies? "

In this way, the government committee reprimands the University of Tokyo seismologists.

Even if there is a reprimand, there is no change in the attitude of the scholar.

At the final council, "Mr. Miyamoto" answered as follows, and the council ended   without making any decisions.

Afterwards, "Mr. Miyamoto" is unclear, but in order to recognize the courage of the teacher, here are some of the testimonies from the Diet deliberations.

For reference, a letter from a member of the Kanoyama Geomagnetic Observatory says "I want to observe it personally". In other words, the understanding of observation methods is deepening.

In connection with that, unfortunately, for example, in this petition, Professor Tsuboi or Professor Hagiwara is opposed. All of them are first-class in seismology, but in this regard, there is at least a little understanding so far, and it is close to the expression that this is not good at all. This has been done to prevent the Meteorological Agency from understanding and proceeding.

Because of such careless remarks by these people, even if some research institution has a desire to push this method even more powerfully, it can be disclosed.

That's part of it.

*

The "Implosive Seismo Detonation" interprets the mechanism by which "geoelectric current" flows because part of the dissociated water becomes "atomic oxygen" and "atomic hydrogen" in the geomagnetic field. In addition, it is interpreted that "MHD power generation" occurs due to movement as a plasma fluid, and local magnetic field changes occur.

A local magnetic field is generated around the earth current, causing the compass to go crazy.

This should be the cause of events such as luminous phenomena, abnormalities in home appliances, abnormal responses in car navigation, abnormal instrumentation in aircraft, abnormal behavior of animals, sparks from reinforcing bars observed in the Tangshan earthquake, etc. is.

*

In the 1976 Tangshan Earthquake, a woman who was watching a thief in the field said, "The sky over about 200 meters suddenly brightened, illuminating the ground, and clearly seeing the leaves and stems of the western foothills. I testified.

It seems that this "luminescence phenomenon" was "42 minutes before" the "earthquake".

It seems that the "high pressure dissociated gas" that was "plasmaized" moved inside the crust before the "explosion" of "dissociated water".

Most of the "Macroscopic anomaly phenomenon" can be explained scientifically.

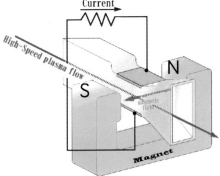

Fig. 7-1 Schematic diagram of "MHD power generation"
Source: http://totoro.ele.tottori-u.ac.jp/text/mhd.html
MHD power generation: Another name is magnetohydrodynamic power generation,
which uses Faraday's law of electromagnetic induction. MHD is short for Magneto-Hydro-Dynamics.

[7-2] "Large noise" heard before "earthquake"

Before an "earthquake", you may hear a suspicious sound like "gorogoro" or "go-go".

According to the story of a local person in Owase who experienced the "1942 Tonankai Earthquake" (the father in the family), the sound of "gorogoro" was heard from the morning offshore when the earthquake occurred.

He thought that an American submarine would be practicing offshore. However, in the afternoon it was hit by a "big earthquake".

This "phantom sound" is not the "air conduction sound" transmitted through the "air" but the "bone conduction sound" that propagates through the "crust", which is equivalent to the human "bone".

This is the same system that can be used with hands-free mobile phones even in noise.

Through the "crust" (bone), the explosion sound in "hypocenter" and the "sound that is reflected and refracted in a complex way" can be heard as "phantom sounds".

By the way, Beethoven, who could not hear "air conduction sound", seemed to be doing music activities using "bone conduction sound".

It is clear that the "fault earthquake theory" is contradictory because there should be no sound before the fault slips.

In the "Tangshan Earthquake", the staff at Tangshan Station testified that they heard a loud "dokan" sounding that everyone trembled.
He would have heard the "earthquake detonation" that occurred right below as "bone conduction sound".

[7-3] Local changes in the "surface" and "atmosphere"

As can be seen from Chapter 1 "Schematic diagram of earthquake mechanism" (Fig.1-2), the pressure of the magma chamber increases by the generation of "dissociation gas" before the "earthquake".

As a result, the underground "hot steam" rises and becomes hot and humid on the ground.
One of the climate greetings is "Today it is hot, so an earthquake may come".

*

(Emperor Tenmu-hakuhou 13) In the Great Earthquake (684) on October 14, "Kuroda-gun" in "Tosa Bay (Kochi Prefecture)" sank.
The record states, "The great earthquakes in each country, then a large field sinks from Tosa's Cape Muroto to Cape Ashizuri and becomes the sea", and the situation of the earthquake is recorded as follows.

112

Even so, this day was so eerie from the morning that it seemed to be calm, clear, clear clouds, no signs of clouds, no wind, and the heat was similar to that in summer. As time passed by the time when people were thinking of strangeness, in the evening sky, the evening sky is now white, milky, no stars shining, and they enter the night. When both of them were subdued, they hit the southeast and screamed and shattered, and people did not feel as much as they thought, and the ground shook. It just seems that the turbulence and heaven and earth will become one.

There are many records that say "It was hot in winter but people wore " single " shirts (summer clothes)".

*

Fig. 7-2 shows the "water vapor column" of the "swarm earthquake off the east of Izu" in July 1989. This photo was taken by a local person five months before the earthquake (February 2).

Fig. 7-2 Water vapor rise observed on the epicenter of the Izu east-offshore earthquake (Teishi Knoll)

The "water vapor" appears to be rising at the location just above the "Teishi Knoll", which became later the "seismic epicenter".

When such "sultry water vapor" drifts to the "surface" and a two-layered air including a "cold air layer" develops above, "Macroscopic anomaly phenomenon" caused by "refractive phenomenon" can be seen. In other words, there are phenomena in old legends such as "the stars looked low and large" or "the moon looked abnormally large".

When the "moon" or "sun" is near "on the horizon," it may appear larger. The Greek "Aristotle" presumed that it would be caused by a "refractive phenomenon", but in the opinion of later scholars, when it was "on the horizon", there was something to compare and it looked big. It is interpreted as an "illusion" and is taught in school as well.
But that's not true.

The refraction of light as it enters the atmosphere from outer space (vacuum) has no effect.

However, if the "two-layer structure of air" can be clarified, it can be proved that the "refractive action" looks large.

The "two-layer structure" where the upper layer is cold and the lower layer is warm is the same setting as looking at the bottom of the lake, just "on the boat" or "from the shore".

Unlike usual, the moon and stars look "big" and low so that the "pond is shallow" and the "fish is big".

A detailed explanation is given at the end of the book as "The reason why the moon on the horizon looks large before the earthquake".

The book "Tangshan Earthquake" contains various incidents such as "The hot spring pond used by workers to bathe was too hot to enter".

[7-4] Local changes in the ionosphere

The "degree of $H2O$ dissosiation" in the deep underground, which is normaly stable, changes depending on "magma rise" and "pressure reduction". The Implosive Seismo Detonation explains that means earthquake occurrence.

This means that the "dissociated gas" is in a "plasma state". As a result, the "underground dissociation layer" may be disturbed, and the "ionosphere" in the sky may change in response to the "change" of the "ionized plasma".

It can be explained that the "listening range" of FM broadcasting changes because the "ionosphere" goes down before the earthquake.

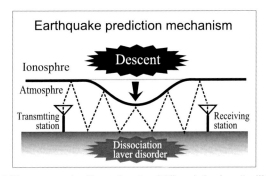

Fig. 7-3 Phenomenon that "ionosphere" and "dissociation layer" will match

From this point of view, the study of "earthquake prediction" promoted by "Dr. Masashi Hayakawa" (Professor Emeritus of the University of Electro-Communications) and "Dr. Takeo Moriya" (Hokkaido University) is considered to be meaningful.

It is desirable not to commit the same foolishness as if the "magnetometer method" of "Dr. Sei Takagi" was buried, sticking to "geodetic earthquake prediction".

It is also known that "airborne ion concentration" increased during the Great East Japan Earthquake. In Sichuan, China, the compass of a military aircraft swung like a sudden mad over 3000 meters during an earthquake.

The pilot did not panic, felt that an "earthquake" would occur, and increased the speed and left the area.

If you have the correct knowledge of earthquakes, you can do this.

[7-5] Launching phenomenon of "dolphins" and "whales"

In Japan, "Dolphin Stranding" has become a hot topic, but there were reports that "a large amount of dolphins" were launched at "The Peruvian sandy beach" and "Iran's Jask coast".

Recently, there are such reports in various places. One of the causes is the "explosion phenomenon" occurring on the "sea floor". In other words, the influence of the "undersea volcano" that does not reach the "sea level" (including seismic phenomena) can be considered.

This may be caused by "burn" caused by "hot water" or "hot gas" erupting from the "sea floor".

(A)　　Fig. 7-4 (A) Peruvian coast (B) Jask coast, Iran　　(B)
Dolphin stranded (presumed to have died from "burn")

Looking at the photos in the case reports of "Peru" and "Iran", it seems that in both cases, "scratches of burns" can be seen in "Dolphin".

Surely, "hot water" is constantly blowing up from the central ridge at the bottom of the sea, but animals such as "dolphins" can avoid such a steady "heat source".

However, the "submarine eruption phenomenon" that suddenly blows up explosively does not have the ability to cope with it, and may be damaged.

Even earthquake events that are not eruptions should be accompanied by a similar "hot water" (hot gas) blow-up if the hypocenter is shallow.

The book "Tsunami Disaster" in "Dr. Yosiaki Kawada" has the following description.

> Suppose you were dragging a "sand beach" with a "tsunami".
> In that case, you may be "big burn" even though you are "in the water".
> Because "sandy beach" is like wet sandpaper. It is because the body is rubbed on it.
> I noticed this when I conducted a survey of the 1998 earthquake and tsunami in Papua New Guinea.
> In hospitals where injured people were carried, there were overwhelmingly more residents with "burns" than "fractures"
> ("Tsunami Disaster" p.4).

While being swept away by the "tsunami," it is unlikely that the sand will be rubbed and burned. Even if it is a hot "sand beach" , if the "tsunami" attacks, it will cool down.

The author considers the earthquake to be "implosive detonation" . Therefore, he thinks that "hot gas" may erupt from the "seabed" and cause burns to the drifting victims.

Also, if it is in the "land area" , it may cause a fire.

In the fault that occurred in the "desert zone", the surrounding dead grass burns.

Recently, earthquakes and volcanic explosions have occurred frequently, but there are many eruptions due to volcanic activity and earthquakes on the sea floor. This is not only "dolphins" and "whales" , but also "deep-sea fish" . This is thought to be the cause of the rising.

*

"Iran's Jask Coast" (Phto. 7-4 (B)) is near the exit of the "Holms Strait" and near the place where the "tanker" of "MOL" was damaged.

The tanker crew says they have witnessed "flash" on the ocean after the "explosion sound".

It is more likely that it was some kind of "natural phenomenon" than a "gas eruption" from the "sea floor" rather than a "pirate attack". The "dolphins" may have been sacrificed.

*

In the "1854 Ansei Great Earthquake", there was a mysterious "explosion phenomenon" in "Ise Bay". According to the record (*)

> On June 15, 1854, there was a major earthquake centered on "Iga", "Ise" and "Yamato". On "13th" and "14th", there were "foreshock activities", both of which were felt in various parts of "Kii Peninsula".

In this document, there is "Ise Ouka, Nishimura saburouemon's letter". Introducing translated sentences.

> There is a story by a crew of "fishing boats" or "ships" that were in the sea on June 14. There were three "black things" flying about 2.5 meters from the sea, and there was also a "fire", and the shipmen were scared and hid at the bottom of the boat. It went up to the beach of "Yokkaichi (Mie Prefecture)", one thinned like smoke and two flew north and west, followed by a "large earthquake".
>
> A person who boarded from "Yokkaichi" came to "Matsusaka (Mie Prefecture)" on the 25th and talked. On the night of the 14th, two "red fireballs" with a diameter of about 9 meters shine from the sea.
> Soon, the "light" disappeared as a lump, and both the sea and the village shook, and the waves turned upside down and were dangerous, but finally the "ship" was brought to the shore and the life was saved.
> In the village, tens of thousands of people shouted, saying that their fear cannot be told.

*

> On the 14th, a person had an errand from "North Ise Nagashima" to "Matsusaka" and rented a "small boat" with five people. He stayed "off the coast" when there was a "serious thing" around "Yokkaichi" .and said.
> Soon after seeing the "light thing" on his right hand, the "wave" turned upside down, and at the same time as the "vibration sound", the "ship overturned", and

both the luggage and the lunch box were thrown into the sea. However, he finally saved his life and returned to Kuwana, but he said he could not reveal the night.

(*) (Disaster prevention science and technology document "Kii Peninsula Earthquake and Tsunami Material")

Ancient Greek scientists believed that the "earthquake" was a "gas eruption phenomenon" .

"Anaxagoras" says that "gas" has a natural "rising" movement, and when it becomes stuck in a "underground hole" , it causes an "earthquake" .

"Dr. Thomas Gold" wrote in "Rethinking the Earthquake" as follows. He was a well-known scientist who knew well that "earthquakes were a gas explosion in the ground".

Seneca wrote that "before the " earthquake " , " the sound of a roar " can be heard well from the " wind " (the flow of air) that is shaking the " underground " .

And, as is often the case with "earthquakes," even if there were only a few "cracks" on the ground (according to what was reported), the "earthquake" that hit "Chalkis" in southeastern Greece. For a few days from there.

I often observed that the "wind" was blowing out.

Seneca was interested in writing his own research on "earthquake" because of the "earthquake" that destroyed Pompeii a lot before the disaster caused by the "eruption" of "Vesuvius" . Because I was shocked. Let me introduce the extraordinary passage that Seneca told me in my words.

Today we interpret it as "caused by the rise of " water vapor " rich in " carbon dioxide "" .

Hundreds of sheep died in the Pompeii region.

... the atmosphere is stagnant ... If you smoke it, you will be killed.

In addition, it is polluted by the "volcano" "fire poison" and if you sit there for a long time, you will get sick later.

... it's no wonder that the sheep are very close to the ground because they are bowed down and are more likely to be attacked by their "poison" (the sheep's body was not made ruggedly). This is because "dirty gas" was blown near the ground.

If more of that "dirty pair" came out, people would have been damaged.

However, many "clean air" wiped out the "dirty" atmosphere, so it did not rise high enough for people to breathe.

Seneca wondered how to explain a series of "aftershocks" (aftershocks) caused by the "Pompeii earthquake" that was felt in the "Campanian region" for several days.

And even if most of them diverge, they conclude that not all the gas erupted in the first eruption, but some are still wandering somewhere in the "underground".

"Isaac Newton" also thought that "earthquake" was related to "gas".

"Water vapor" containing "sulfur" fills the inside of a round earth, reacts with "mineral", and suddenly "ignites" or "explodes".

If it is confined to an "underground cave", it will "blow up" the cave and shake the earth a lot like a "mine explosion"

Wrote Newton.

Also noteworthy is the following description in the first edition of Britannica published in 1771.

"In the "Earthquake Museum", a significant part of the Earth shakes violently, and there is often a terrible sound like "Thunder", and fire and water may erupt."

In Japan, there is a record of "gas eruption" similar to the West.

Both "dolphin burns" and "tanker damages" are highly likely to be the culprit.

"Seismology theory" should be able to explain these "natural phenomena associated with earthquakes".

"Implosive Seismo Detonation" is convinced that it is a theory that can explain many phenomena well.

Chapter 8

Truth of "Earth Structure"

Mankind has entered an era of interest in the moon and Mars.
But people don't know much about the essential Earth.
In addition to the fact that the "mantle" is solid, we don't know why
granites exist only on Earth or why they are produced only on the continent.
In the earthquake theory based on Hydrogen Implosion,
the mystery will be solved at once.
There is a big difference depending on whether hydrogen and
oxygen exist in the combined water state or separate state
before the magma solidifies.

The big point is that there is a "heat-retaining mechanism"
called ocean.
The fact that ancient civilizations such as Atlantis and
Mu existed on the earth is also due to the stubborn theory of
"Solid Geophysics" that makes the thinking stop.
Need to be resurrected.

[8-1] The inside of the earth is "Magma Ocean"

As said in this book, the "inside of the earth" mantle is "melting".
It is natural to assume "Earth History" since "Earth Birth".
In other words, the "Primitive Earth" should have been in the state of "Magma Ocean".

Since there are various theories such as "theories separated from the sun" and "theories in which the fragments of stars are gathered", the state before that is not discussed here. However, there must be no doubt that it was "Magma Ocean".

After that, "cooling" progressed, "magma" "solidified" like a thin skin, and "crust" should be formed.
There should be no objection to the birth of the "ocean", the survival of "animals and plants", and the birth of "humanity".

Therefore, the "inside of the earth" excluding the crust on the surface should still be in the state of "magma ocean".
At the same time as the formation of the crust, the cooling and solidification of the Earth Mantle can not proceed simultaneously.

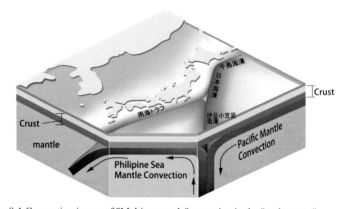

Fig. 8-1 Convection image of "Melting mantle" occurring in the "under crust"

*

In the current theory, deep earthquake areas are related to plate subduction. Ishida's theory (Hydrogen Imploson theory) interprets that magma is convection in the form of ocean currents in the sea of magma. (magma-ocean)

In other words, it is like a "sea current" in the "melting mantle" that should be called "Philippine Sea Mantle Convection" or "Pacific Mantle Convection".

It seems strange why "plate theorists" are bound by "mantle solid theory". Actually, it is only constrained by "prerequisites for computer analysis".

[8-2] Controversy between "horizontal" (A) and "vertical" (B)

So what has happened since the first "continent" and "the ocean" were created? Here, the opinions are largely divided.

(A) Horizontal movement group / mobilist
The group thinks that the "continent" will "split" and repeat "move" in the "horizontal direction".
(B) Vertical lift / fixist
This group believes that the "continent" repeats "up and down" vertically.
Two groups were arguing during the "Cold War Structure of the US-Soviet Union".

*

The "horizontal" in (A) is "Wegener" who advocated the "continent movement theory" that became the basis of "Plate Technics" and was a scholar on the Western side, like "Professor Wilson".
The "vertical group" in (B) was a scholar on the east side, with Soviet "Prof. Beloussov" as the representative.

In Japan, many geophysicists were "horizontal" and many geologists were "vertical".

(1908–1993)
Wilson
John Tuzo

(1907–1990)
Beloussov
Vladimir Vladimirovich

Fig. 8-2 Wilson and Beloussov (controversial rivals)

Judging from the knowledge of Hydrogen Implosion, the "horizontal" judgment that "Africa" and "South America" were divided is correct. However, there is no evidence that it happened "on the whole earth."

On the whole of the earth, rather than the "vertical ups and downs" that the "vertical group" was thinking, it can be said that it is "mainstream" as "crustal movement".

However, it does not support the "Tikousya theory" that the "vertical group" was thinking.

We cannot clearly determine which is correct. However, in other words, the "horizontal group" looked too much at the "special phenomenon" of the "special place", for example, it was too much about the "special solution of the differential equation". On the other hand, the "vertical group" may have stuck to the "general solution" and "denied" the "special solution". Neither solution is a mistake.

[8-3] What is the difference between the "continental crust" and the "oceanic crust"?

Let's look at the difference between the "oceanic crust" and the "continental crust".

As a general perception,
· Continental crust
The "crust layer" is thick. There is a light granite in the upper part
· Oceanic crust
The "crust layer" is thin. There is a heavy "basalt" at the top

It is said that.

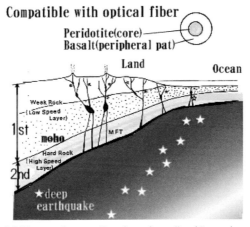

Fig. 8-3 Differences between "continental crust" and "oceanic crust"

In the "current theory", the mantle is defined below the "Moho boundary".

However, in reality, there is a layer of "Pendolite rock" that propagates "seismic waves" quickly under the "Moho boundary", and below that should be a "melting mantle" — that is, "magma ocean" is.

By the way, there are "granite" ("sialic") in the "continent" and "basalt" ("sima") in the "ocean". How to explain this is one major problem in earth science, and it is a big mystery.

Sial means that it contains Si, Al (silica, aluminum)
Shima means that it contains Si and Mg (silica, magnesium)

They can't explain the exact reason, but it looks as if the light sialic "continent" is floating on heavy pelitic basalt. From this, the concept of "isostasy" was born and helped to create the concept of horizontal "plate theory".

Of course, the concept of "isostasy" is wrong.

The concept of "hydrostatic mechanics" cannot be applied to "solid mechanics".

Here, We will solve the mystery of why "granite" is only generated on "continent" "and" why it exists only on the earth with "sea", not on other stars ".

[8-4] "Floating" of the "continent" (continentalization)

"Granite" and "basalt" are not so different in composition as shown in Table 1.

It can be said that the difference in density is due to the difference in crystal structure, not the component composition.

Granite is characterized by the growth of crystals and is thought to be produced over time in the presence of water (H_2O).

Since "atoms" are arranged with a fixed structure, "density" is naturally small.

In addition, because "supercritical water" has a large solubility, the "chemical composition" varies depending on the difference between solubility and supercritical water content.

Table 1 Composition table of "Granite" and "Basalt"

Ingredient	Granite	Basalt
SiO2	70%	50%
Al2O3	15%	15%
Iron oxide	3%	9%
MgO	1.5%	9%

During the process of "cooling" and "solidifying" from melted magma, it seems to have different components from "basalt".

In this way, "granite" is slowly "cooled" in an environment where there is sufficient "water H2O", so that "crystallization" proceeds, and that beautiful whitish "granite" (a stone that is a flower and a rigid stone?).

The "continent" is the place that was originally "ocean". It is possible to float on the surface of the sea by increasing volcanic activity.

The "crust" is thin when it is on the "sea floor", and below it is the "melting mantle".

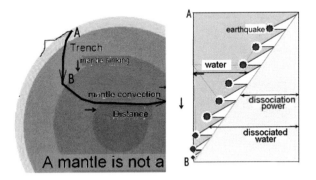

Fig.8-4 Content ratio of "dissolved water" and "bound water" in the mantle

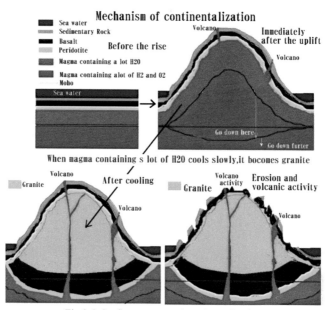

Fig.8-5 Seafloor ascent and continentalization

The ratio of bound water and dissociated water in the "mantle" was also described in Chapter 1. In the "upper part of the mantle", there is more "bound water H2O", and in the "lower part" there is more "dissociated water".

When this "mantle material" emerges and is exposed to the atmosphere, cooling proceeds.

Since seawater does not move on the sea floor, cooling does not proceed. Therefore, the "crust" is thin, but in the air, "cooling" also proceeds because the air flow is fast .

In this way, the "crust" that has emerged and "continentalized" becomes thicker as crystallization progresses.

Under the "sediment" and "basalt" that once existed on the surface of the "ocean crust" , "granite" was born.

Furthermore, under the "granite" , mantle material with a high content ratio of dissociated water cools. However, because there is no H2O there, it is difficult to crystallize (granite) and solidify as "basalt" .

It will take tens of thousands of years for the subsurface crust to appear on the earth's surface, which requires continental ascent and erosion.

[8-5] "Sinking" of the "continent" (oceanization)

On the other hand, consider the case where the "continent" sinks to the ocean floor.

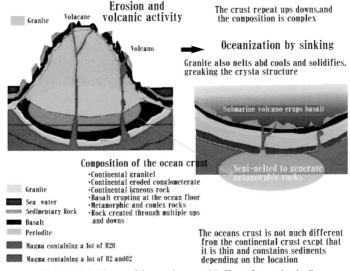

Fig.8-6 Subsidence of the continent and "effect of oceanization"

While it exists as the "continent," there are some places where "granite" forms roadsides under various "erosion" effects. There are also places where "basalt" forms "land" due to "volcanic activity".

The "continent" , which has undergone a complex transition, also "submerges" in a series of "big earthquakes" (giant implosions) called "horizontal explosion (energy release)" . Then, the heat release from the crust decreases, and the "crust" becomes thinner. In other words, the crust melts again.

Once the rock has been "solidified", it is melted again to form "metamorphic rock".

In the semi-molten state, the "parallel stratum" can also be "folded" by the influence of "submarine earthquake", "covered" (decking), and various "deformations".

This shows the various "geological structures" on the ground during the next "continentalization".

In this way, the "continental crust" of granite remains on the "ocean floor". There will also be a new "basalt plateau" that erupts from submarine volcanoes.

There is a difference between the "ocean bottom" and the "continent" that can be made by the "difference in cooling effect"— that is, "thickness". Basically, "Shinkai 6500" (Japanese marine research ship) was taught to say "no difference".

The "Shinkai 6500" dived in the "Rio Grande Rise" off the coast of Brazil.

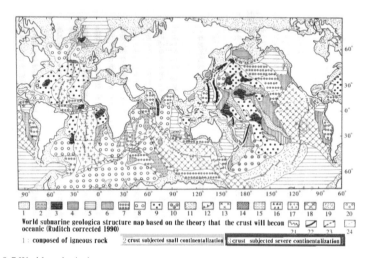

Fig. 8-7 World geological map
  It was already known that there was a "terrestrial crust" on the "seabed" around the world, and a continental crust off the coast of Brazil.

130

This place is known as the "continental crust" in the book "Searching for a New Earth" (Aichi Publishing), which has been subjected to intense "oceanic action".

As shown in Figure 8-7, the "oceanic bottom" of the world has been found to have "continental crust" in many places.

The fact that it was confirmed as a video in the "submarine survey" would be a big opportunity to change the "view of the earth".

The NHK report states that:

Is it related to "Atlantis"? The traces of the continent on the seabed

May 7, 2013

Announced by the Japan Agency for Marine-Earth Science and Technology, which conducted a field survey stating that there was a trace of a large land like the land on the Atlantic Ocean floor in Brazil's offshore did.

The relationship with the legendary continent "Atlantis", which is said to have been sunk in the sea in ancient times, is drawing attention.

The Japan Marine Research and Development Organization used a submersible research ship "Shinkai 6500" last month to investigate a plateau approximately "1500 km offshore" southeast of "Rio de Janeiro". They collaborated with "Brazil Research Institute".

As a result, we found a "rock cliff" on the ocean floor, which is about 900 meters deep. Analyzing the image reveals that the "rock" was a "granite" formed only on land.

In addition, a large amount of "sand that came out of minerals" called "quartz" that could not be found in the sea was found around this cliff.

Since the width of the plateau at the bottom of the sea is about 1000 kilometers, the ocean research and development mechanism states that it seems to be a trace of a large land like a continent.

In the "Atlantic" where the investigation was conducted, there was a theory that the ancient Greek philosopher Plato had the legendary continent "Atlantis", which he wrote in the book, "Sinked into the sea about 12,000 years ago" There is.

The granite discovered this time seems to have sunk into the sea about 50 million years ago, and although there is a chronological shift, it is attracting attention that it may be somehow related.

Mr. Hiroshi Kitasato, the leader of the field research and the "Japan Agency for Marine-Earth Science and Technology," said, "I was really surprised and moved when I was able to see the granite on the bottom of the sea. It seems to be a different discovery, but I think it is a meaningful discovery that found the "continental fragment" in the Atlantic Ocean. "

There is no conclusion in the myth that the light "granite" (sial) is on the "continent" and the "ocean" has only heavy "basalt" (sima).

"Granite" is thought to be produced only on the "continent" , so the discovery of "Shinkai 6500" has an impact.

[8-6] Failure of "plate tectonics theory"

The explanation is unnecessary, but the fact that the "plate tectonics theory" has failed is proved by the expansive "granite plateau" discovered by the research ship "Shinkai 6500" .

There have been many examples of "granite" being collected from the "ocean bottom" . Each time, various "escapes" have been made. For example, "Ore carrier has dropped" or "There was a time when glaciers were developing on the surface of the earth, and those glaciers carried that time" .

However, if such a vast plateau is found, it is no longer possible.

In the past, the author introduced that the "Rockall Plateau" in the Atlantic Ocean is an "old rock" of "540 million years" . At that time, one commented that the "continental shelf" was partly "separated," so it could not be generally "disproved" for "plate tectonics" . The vast "Rio Grande Rise" with a width of 1000km cannot be argued that a part of the "continental shelf" was "separated" .

There are various forms of "proof of failure of the plate theory". For

Fig. 8-8 Map of Rio Grande Rise off Brazil

example, the nature of "residual geomagnetism" is different between the upper, middle, and lower layers of the "crust", or "old rocks have a life expectancy of 200 million years," which is evidence of the "ocean bottom expansion theory". There is a lot of evidence, so you may not need to submit any more "proof of mistake".

"GPS" has confirmed that "Hawaii" is approaching "Japan" at a speed of several millimeters a year, and this has been one of the strong evidences.

However, don't forget to look at the observations that "Japan and Germany are getting closer", which should be on the same plate.

The information on the "ground movement" provided by "GPS" is the information on the "skin movement" in humans, so to speak, it does not tell the fluctuation of the "skeleton" called "the crust". There is none.

[8-7] Evidence that tells the rise and fall of the continent

There is some evidence that the "continent" "rises" or "sinks". This is proof that the intuition of "verticals" was correct.

The "Grand Canyon" repeats "three times of ups and downs" and it can be seen from its "stratum" (Fig. 8-9).

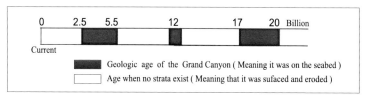

Fig. 8-9 Evidence for "subsidence" and "levitation" of the Grand Canyon

The "red part" in Fig. 8-9 is the age when "fossil" exists as the "stratum" .
In the age of the "white part" , there is no "stratum" .
This means that it was "surfaced" , that is, an era when it was exposed to natural phenomena of "weathering" and "erosion" .

[8-8] Contradiction of "isostasy"

The "current theory" has the concept of "isostasy" . This includes the contradiction of applying "Archimedes' principle" to "Solid mechanics" which is "Mechanics of still water".

Supporters of the "current theory" are "thought restraints" that the mantle is solid. Nevertheless, they believe that the light "granite" on the "continent" is deeply rooted. Furthermore, the illusion that the "light continent" floats on the "heavy ocean bottom basalt" has fallen. .
However, it is a nonsense concept from the viewpoint of "dynamics" .

As mentioned in "continentalization" , it looks like a "root" under the high mountains of the continent because the "cooling power" increases as the "high mountains" . Therefore, "granite" is formed at the bottom of "high mounteains" .

The result of investigating "gravity anomaly" while crossing the "Andes Mountains" by car can be found in the book "Introduction to Earthquakes,

Plates, Land and Oceanography" by Dr. Yoshio Fukao.

The negative "Bouguer anomaly" is very similar to the "mountain shape" , and it can be estimated that light rocks such as "granite" have spread under the Andes.

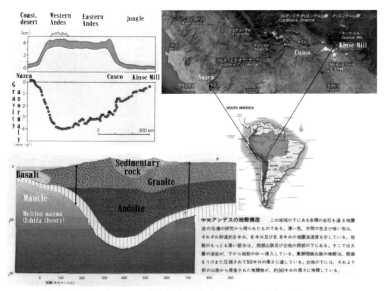

Fig.8-10 "Gravity anomaly" in the "Andean Highlands" and its reasons

There is an explanation that the "Himalayan Mountains" have been pushed by the "India-Australia Plate" and are still increasing by a few millimeters a year.

The explanation of "Plate theory supporter" explains that the plate moves because of the mechanism that the cold and heavier plate "pulls down" the tablecloth from "under the table" . .

In the so-called "active movement theory" , why does the dragged plate push up the mountain? It cannot be explained. The theory cannot explain it.

Rather, under "high mountains" such as "Himalayan" and "Andes" , "crystallization" is still deep underground. It is a reasonable interpretation to assume that "granite" continues to form and that the mountains may be several millimeters higher.

On the other hand, in "Greenland" and "Antarctica" , the "ice sheet" has disappeared, and the "plateau" is beginning to be exposed.

There is a report that "ground" is "raised" due to "rebound" due to the load of the ice sheet.

However, it is also necessary to consider that "cooling of the crust" will proceed more than before by exposing it to the atmosphere. In other words, it can be seen that "the continentalization is progressing further in the deep underground" rather than the viewpoint of "raising" with the reaction of "heavy stone" . It ' s a reasonable interpretation.

The "inside of the snow cave" is "warm" than the wind-swept "snow top" and protects you from distress.

In years when there is little "snow", the wheat that was sown in the fall will dic due to "coldness" and will be unsuccessful. With the same reason,

・ The crust at the bottom of the ocean does not cool and the crust is thin.

・ The higher the altitude of the continental crust, the higher the air cooling effect by strong winds, and the crust is thick.

[8-9] What the distribution of "rock salt deposit" means

Everywhere on the earth, there are places where you can "mine" "rock salt" .

The "rock salt deposit" was once the "ocean" .

(1) At least once, it "floated" to "Land" and was dried in the sun to become a "salt lump" .

(2) Just like the "Grand Canyon" , it can be made a place where the

"floating" was repeated many times.

The above is common sense.

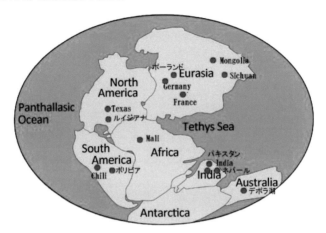

Fig. 8-11 "Illusion of Pangea" taught by "Salt Deposit"

Fig. 8-11 is a plot of the "Salt Deposit" that is currently being mined on top of "Pangea".

"Pangea" is a fictitious continent that existed 200 to 300 million years ago.

Clearly, the "Salt Deposit" is distributed all over the world.

However, the formation of " rock salt " is a story hundreds of millions of years before the formation of " Pangea " sounds like an unreasonable excuse.

This is also why "vertical" is more correct than "horizontal".

In addition, plotting "where ammonite can be collected" will be clear.

Ammonite is a fossil of "aquatic life" that can be collected in Japan. There should have been a sea.

[8-10] Deep drilling of the crust is dangerous

Now, from the commentary so far, you will be worried that "the extraction and excavation of submarine resources" is planned without knowing that the inside of the earth is melting.

"JAMSTEC" deep-sea drilling vessel "Chikyu " is currently making a big success and boasts high performance as follows.

Deep-sea investigation using Chikyu
Chikyu is the world's first "riser-type scientific drilling vessel" that enables "deep drilling" into "mantles" and "large earthquake occurrence areas" for the first time in human history.
Chikyu is conducting Earth exploration as the main ship of the Integrated International Deep Sea Drilling Program (IODP).
(Omitted)

The earth records the traces of the past that clearly show the history of "climate change", "biological activities", and "crustal deformation".
Chikyu aims to achieve various results to open up the future of humanity. For example, "Earthquake mechanism" , "Environmental change of the earth's scale" , "Subsurface life zone supported by global energy" , "Elucidation of new submarine resources" .

It is a pleasure to have high performance, but a warning must be issued for leaving "ignorance" about "inside the earth" and doing "big activity".

The "oil drilling accident" in the Gulf of Mexico is a new memory.

Without knowing that the "mantle" is "molten" , drilling the "deep seabed" with only "the ability to extract mantle material" will cause serious "environmental destruction" .

Drilling will never be possible to the true "melting mantle" and will fail eventully.

However, "an accident like the Gulf of Mexico" must not be caused by the approval of "an established authority scholar" who is ignorant about the earth.

According to reports of the "Kola Peninsula" that failed to drill into the mantle, the "drilling drill" melted and fell, and ultimately the workers were afraid of the "devil roar". And they ran away.

The "Kola Peninsula Ultra Deep Drilling Mine" is a "scientific drilling plan" conducted by the Soviet Union to investigate the "deep part of the earth's crust".

On May 24, 1970, "excavation" started in the "Kola Peninsula", and several "support shafts" were excavated from the "main mine".

At the deepest, it reached 12,261 meters, which was then the world record (1989).

Initially, the plan was for a depth of 15,000 meters, but it was abandoned in 1992 when it encountered an unforeseen ground temperature of 180 °C.

It has also been reported that a large amount of "hydrogen" was stored in the "mineway".

Below is an introduction to the "Drilling Report".

Scientists have made a great discovery in the "ultra-deep" hole of "Kola"

http://orthodoxengland.org.uk/demonsscr.htm

In 2006, "The 25th Anniversary of the Cola Drilling Project" was held at Zapolyarny Station in the vicinity of Murmansk in the Arctic region. The celebration was held.

In 1983, although it had reached a depth of 12 kilometers, it took 10 years to dig another 262 meters by 1995 when the project was frozen.

Already scientists have discovered many "fossilized microorganisms" from very deep locations, reaching a depth of 4 km, and have realized that everything that textbooks have predicted is wrong.

There was no "basalt", but there was a lot of "granite", and all "temperatures" were higher than expected.

At a depth of 10 kilometers, scientists have discovered wonderful deposits called "gold" and "diamonds".

"Temperature" at a depth of "12 kilometers" was "220 degrees Celsius" higher than expected, and there was a significant amount of "heat dissipation" that would destroy many "titanium drills" .

Currently, there are five scientists stationed at the deepest hole research facility on Earth in "Cola" , and they are examining "substances dug from the bottom of the Earth" .

In effect, the "underground excavation project" underway around the world has been completed when it reaches a depth of 3 kilometers.

Of these, 600times were performed by "America" , "Germany" , and "Japan" , but as soon as the "cursed depth" was reached, "mysterious events" began to occur.

In some cases, the "drill" burned indefinitely, and in other cases, it was pulled down by the "invisible force" and "disappeared" .

Around the world, only "5 holes" are deeper than "3 kilometers" , of which "4" are in "Soviet" .

"Oil" and "gas" were stored in the hole, but only the "Cola" hole was dug deeper than "7 kilometers" . At that "depth" , "70 hours" are required to extract the "substance sample" of the earth.

It takes "one minute" for "temperature" , "heat dissipation" , and "noise" to reach the surface.

When the "Cola" "Deep Drilling Hole" reaches a depth of "10 kilometers" , many "wonderful events" occur in the "deepest part" .

Although the "tip" of the "titanium drill" can only be melted by the "temperature of the solar surface" , the "tip of the drill" "melted" twice.

The "drill" was "pulled" to break down many times and broke, and the "drill tip" was never found.

These are just a few examples of unexplained events.

In particular, a "strange noise" was heard from the bottom of the planet in 1994, before reaching the depth of "13 kilometers" and closing the borehole.

Those who heard it unanimously argued that the noise could not be considered other than "the cry of sinners in hell."

After that, there was a very large "explosive sound" that was difficult to explain, and the story of the devil appearing from the bottom of the earth spread.

The project was frozen in 1995 because workers refused to work any more because the devil was on the ground.

Sadly, the "digger" says that a sound similar to "screaming" has risen from the bottom to the ground.

In the spring of this year, a scientist from the Geophysical Laboratory was sent to

Cola for further surprising discoveries. It is said that "sounds of human activity" have been heard from a depth of 3 kilometers.

In other words, it can be said that those who live in "hell" know exactly what is going on among those who live on the surface of this planet .

At a depth of 12000 meters, water "dissociates" into "oxygen" and "hydrogen" .

If "pressure" decreases locally by drilling "mine" , "dissociation water" will rebound and return to "water" "explosion phenomenon" – that is, a small "earthquake" can be estimated.

The fact that the "digging mine" is filled with water, the "hydrogen concentration" is high, and the "explosion noise" in the narrow mine produces an unusual "resonance sound" can be explained scientifically. It has nothing to do with devil screams.

The fact that the "drill" "melts" or disappears can be convinced that the "dissociation gas" is a "mixed gas" of ionized "oxygen" and "hydrogen" .

This means that a reaction in the "plasma state" is occurring. It resembles the mysterious reaction of "Brown Gas" .

The result from Hydrogen Implosion is that we would like to stop the dangerous act of digging the "ocean bottom" aiming at the "moho surface" without misunderstanding "earth structure" .

[8-11] Seismic region anomaly of "deep earthquake"

When a "deep earthquake" (inner mantle earthquake) occurs in the vicinity of Japan, the problem of "abnormal seismic zone" always occurs.

This phenomenon of "seismic region anomaly" occurs because the "mantle" is not solid and the "crustal thickness" is not constant.

It seems strange at first glance, but understands that the "crustal structure" is a "two-layer structure" as shown in Fig. 2-6 or Fig.8-3, and that the "crustal thickness" is not constant near the trench. You can see that this is not an abnormal phenomenon.

"Deep earthquakes" do not pass through the "current theory" (curved course) shown in Figure 2-6, but propagate through the "second crust" (high propagation speed) under the "Moho surface". Therefore, it propagates faster than "nolmal calculated value". You can be convinced that "runtime residue minus" (meaning to arrive early).

In addition, as can be understood from Fig. 8-3, the hard and dense "second layer" is located near the "surface" in the entire area from "Kanto" to "Tohoku" and "Hokkaido".

The "P wave" of "deep earthquake" or "S wave" generated by the "P wave" entering the "crustal second layer" propagates through the sensitive "second layer".

In the "deep earthquake" of the "Japan Sea" and "Southern Okhotsk Sea", the epicenter is insensitive. However, the "Kanto" and "Tohoku" can become "sensitive".

In Japan, "Eastern" is more sensitive than "West".

An increase in the "seismic intensity" at a location away from the "epicenter" can also occur in a "shallow earthquake". The reason is that the "push cone axis" is "tilted" and the "point intersecting the ground" is far from the epicenter.

However, the "abnormal seismic zone" of "deep earthquakes" near Japan is caused by a completely different "crustal structure".

Appendix 1

Safety awareness of RITE CO2 geological storage plan (CCS) manager

This section introduces the "safety awareness" held by the project leader of the "CO2 underground storage plan" and the contents of the reply e-mail from the "Ishida Institute Director".

Of course, the engineers on the ground are planning the plan by believing the words of academic experts, but we must not forget that science still has unknown elements.

Project leader

Regarding the matter you pointed out, we will judge that it is inappropriate due to the following reasons (three items).

Please provide appropriate opinions and responses based on scientific evidence, not speculation from overseas cases with completely different geological and geophysical conditions.

Reply (Ishida Research Institute Director)

The scientific grounds are very important, but all the cases in which companies have been pursuing social responsibility so far have their causes in the so-called unknown science field, which was scientifically unknown at that time. Wasn't it?

"I didn't know at that time …" I think it has been repeatedly apologized after many tragedy.

Certainly, at this time, seismologists testify that "the fault moves and becomes an earthquake," so for now there is a causal relationship between the injection of material (liquid) into the basement and the occurrence of an earthquake.

However, in the unknown science that will be revealed in the future, it may be impossible to say that there is no causal relationship. It does not take into account the company's responsibilities that are asked at that time.

Even if legal liability is exempted as " I couldn't have foreseen ...",I don't know if it is exempt from moral responsibility. Because it is accompanied by difficult life and tragedy of many citizens.

First item

The hypocenter of the Niigata Chuetsu Earthquake is about 10km. It is about 20km away from the "Iwanohara Base", where we are conducting a test for injecting carbon dioxide. On the other hand, the depth of the aquifer that stores carbon dioxide is about 1,100m, and the expansion of CO2 in the aquifer is about 100m from the inlet.

The "Iwanohara Base" is also far from the aftershock area of the Chuetsu Earthquake, so it is not realistic to think that it caused the earthquake.

Reply (Ishida Research Institute Director)

We recognize that the epicenter and the injection site are separated. However, the water that is pushed out by the injected CO2 moves along the water vein. This causes a problem that the ability of water to thermally dissociate deeply changes.

Since the deeper the underground, the higher the ability to dissociate, it is thought that dissociation gas may be generated if water in a shallow area is continuously pushed into it.

Second item

In the demonstration test, the pressure of supercritical CO2 stored in an aquifer 1,100m underground is constantly observed. After the start of press-fitting, there was no pressure fluctuation that would have been caused by an explosion (implosion).

We are also conducting basic research on the chemical reaction between injected supercritical CO2 and minerals, and have confirmed that such an event does not occur.

The Chuetsu earthquake is a reverse-stratified earthquake that has a maximum principal stress axis in the direction of west-northwest and east-east. The analysis from seismic waves shows that the fault occurred when the fault slipped up and down.

Reply (Ishida Research Institute Director)

CO2 is not a direct cause of explosion, but the explosion (implosion) of dissociated gas that breaks away from water that has continuously moved to the deep underground becomes a problem.

Therefore, it is profitable that there is no pressure fluctuation due to explosion (implosion) in the observation area by the measuring instrument. I think that the phenomenon of thermal dissociation has nothing to do with the chemical reaction with minerals.

It is common knowledge of seismology that the cause of an earthquake is fault slip, but the story changes according to another oxyhydorogen detonation theory.

Third item

At Iwanohara Station, microtremors are observed. There is no correlation between the press-in rate, cumulative press-in amount, and the occurrence of fine movement.

Reply (Ishida Research Institute Director)

In Denver, waste liquid is injected directly up to 3800m underground.

Since it is 1100m at the Iwanohara base, it is quite possible that there will be a time difference in order to affect the dissociation gas generation point.

Deliberation of academics

This research and development has been deliberated by the Carbon Dioxide Underground Storage Technology Research and Development Promotion Committee, chaired by Professor Emeritus of the University of Tokyo.

We are promoting demonstration tests based on discussions based on scientific evidence from teachers who are members of academic background.

Reply (Ishida Research Institute Director)

No matter what kind of academic experience you have, since you are all members of unknown science, you would say, "At that time, scholars didn't know." In addition, even if scholars deliberately eliminate legal liability, moral responsibility may remain.

I am most worried that the knowledge about the cause of the earthquake may be wrong, which may cause easy man-made work deep underground and cause a lot of tragedy.

I would be happy if you could reconsider the above.

March 2005 Director, Ishida Earthquake Research Institute

Appendix 1

Reason why the moon on the horizon looks large before the earthquake

The following questions are on the NAOJ site

http://www.nao.ac.jp/faq/a0202.html

Question 2-2) Why does the moon and the sun look bigger?
For that, the following answers are listed.

> There are many experiences that the moon and the sun look big. It seems that the moon and the sun at that time are often near the horizon.
> However, the size has not really changed. The moon and sun are always about the same size no matter where you are in the sky. (Omitted)
> It is said that due to the optical illusion that the moon and the sun look large when they are close to the horizon.
> However, there is still no clear explanation why this illusion occurs.
> Some people say that the view of buildings and mountains can be seen near the moon, and that the size can be felt differently when compared to it.

Finally, they are cleaning up with "Moon Illusion".

The reason why the "illusion" occurs is that there is no "conventional theory".

"Aristotle" should have been called a "refractive phenomenon", but that seems to be denied in the current science. Is science really progressing?

Certainly, even if the "moonlight" jumps from the "vacuum universe" into the "atmosphere", the bending there is not a problem, so the "refraction theory" of "Aristotle" was denied.

However, the "Implosive Seismo Detonation" presents that the moon is sure to look red and large as a "predictor of a massive earthquake".

I want to insist that it is not.

Of course, it can happen even if the warm humid air from the south gets into the "two-layer structure", so the fact that the moon looks large is not a "predictor of the earthquake".

The "moon" looks red because the "water vapor" contained in the sultry air scatters short-wavelength blue systems, so that only long-wavelength red waves enter the human eye.

It looks red due to the same reasoning as the "sunset phenomenon".
Sometimes the moon looks red, it may be a sign of an earthquake, or it
may not. Even if yellow sand is flying from China, it will look red.

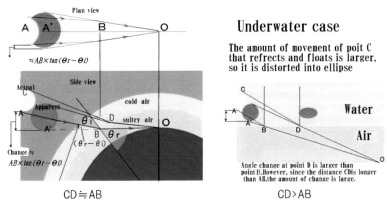

Fig.-Appendix

Now, if the size changes due to refraction, there are those who firmly
believe that the shape of the moon should be distorted because the shape
of the moon is different vertically and horizontally so that the ball in water
looks like an ellipse. .

We will solve that problem first.

Basically check the difference between a sphere and a plane. Looking at
the moon under a two-layer structure of cold and sultry air is similar to
looking at an underwater ball, but there is a difference between a sphere
and a plane.

When looking at the water, the ball will appear flat and horizontally
long. The reason is, for example, the amount by which the upper surface A
of the ball floats can be approximated by ABtan (θr-θi) using Snell's law.

θr is the refraction angle and θi is the incident angle. The human eye is at point O. On the other hand, the amount that the bottom C of the ball floats is CDtan (θr-θi). The angle variation of (θr-θi) is larger at point B than at point D, but because it is a flat surface, the distance is CD> AB, and the lower surface C of the ball appears to float higher. In other words, the ball will appear distorted.

If you look at the moon or the sun, the effect is that the earth is a sphere. The amount CD tan (θr-θi) that lowers the upper end C of the moon and the amount AB tan (θr-θi) that lowers the lower end A are almost the same value because AB $\doteqdot$ CD. In other words, the moon does not look distorted even if it is refracted.

Here, consider the case where the refractive index of cold air is 1.00028 and the refractive index of sultry air is 1.00025 (temperature difference 25 degrees, humidity difference 50%).
When the hot air layer is 1km above the sky, magnification is 6%, 500m is 10%, 300m is 14%, and 100m is 25%.
If a hot air layer with a temperature difference of 25 degrees is formed into a two-layer structure, you can see that the moon is likely to look large.

This calculation is not exact. This is an approximate calculation that does not take into account that the point D where the light at the top edge C of the moon is refracted moves slightly away from B. However, there is no problem qualitatively explaining that the moon appears to expand.
The above approximate calculation is when the incident angle θi and the refraction angle θr are close to 90 degrees, that is, when the moon is near the horizon (same for the sun). If it rises higher, the approximation calculation becomes invalid.
An old person who could not prove it would have told: Just before the big earthquake, hot water erupted from the ground and drifted in a layer of about 100m in the low sky with a high temperature difference, or in a sultry night, the moon and stars were large, and the stars were always

sparkling.

Even if seismologists ignore it, the legend of the old man may be meaningful.

It is unfortunate that even the precious legend has been treated the same as the optical illusion because the reason why the moon on the horizon looks large can not be explained.

Reference: Calculation method of magnification

Target when the lowest end of the apparent moon is visible on the horizon.

If the angle which B point and O point make with the earth center is calculated, the refraction angle at B point will be decided.

Determining the angle of incidence from Snell's law determines the angle increment due to refraction, and the amount by which the lowest end of the moon apparently drops.

At the top of the moon, the incident angle is the value reduced by the parallax of the moon, and the refraction angle is obtained from Snell's formula. In the same way as above, the amount of apparent fall of the top of the moon is determined from the angle increment due to refraction. The difference is the amount that the moon apparently expanded.

This will determine the enlargement ratio. The amount of parallax increase is also determined.

Afterword

At present, the author does not belong to any academic society other than "Earthquake explosion theory society".

It is not "in a Diogenes's barrel", but it is just one private person who lives in an apartment like a "barrel".

However, as Takamori Saigo says, I want to have the belief that "people who don't need life, don't need a name, and don't need government or money can't be defeated."

Therefore, without this "belief", I believe that the great work of the "Seismological Revolution" cannot be accomplished with difficulty.

The author estimates that this book will be greeted with a great "rejection" by "Seismologists" and "Media".

But if he says "I'm not afraid of anything", does it sound like a lie?

Respected "Dr. Mishio Ishimoto" wrote in the "Storybook about Galileo" as follows:

Galileo recognized that the simplicity of Copernicus's astronomical system is wonderful that convinces many things. However, he was afraid of becoming a subject of "criticism" and "riding", and for the time being, he stoped expressing his "approval of ground motion".

And bravely,

Scientific breakthroughs always begin with a "new theory proposal".
However, in order to establish a new theory, it is necessary to be prepared to accept the "old theory" and ultimately the intense opposition to the crushing action.
Even great scholars in the past rarely failed to be treated this way.
If you are faithful to the "theory" that you believe, you should not lose power or throw away your thoughts.
It is good to reflect on the other party's opinions and reflect on yourself, but throwing out what you believe must be considered a sneaky act than going down to the military gate. (From "discussion with scholars"

The author is in a year to get a pension, so there should be nothing scary.

Therefore, according to the words of "Dr. Ishimoto", I want to stay in a steady posture without disturbing my heart.

However, as I appealed in the election campaign, when I accuse the "obscene premonition" performed by "politicians", "great bureaucrats", and "media", public anger comes to my heart.

The "pension" was supposed to have been accumulated in the hope of an independent elder life, but soon it switched to the "payment system" and was accused of "helping each other".

Therefore, it is regrettable that we have to feel the negative of "a pension" supported by the "young generation".

Other than that, there is nothing disturbed.

The phrase "Issai Sato" (famous Confucian in Edo) has the phrase "The praise is imaginary and real. However, the actual achievement is a work that will take a lifetime". I want to keep this in my heart and repel ridicule.

The motivation for writing this book came from those who attended the lecture. He sent me an email like this:

> This is the time when "theoretical seismology" has lost the most trust, and an alternative is needed. Since society does not know "Ishida Seismology", it is a situation in which people with heart are also going right and left. I ask Dr. Ishida to publish a general book of "Earthquake Oxyhydorogen Detonation" as soon as possible.

I received an e-mail with this content.

To be sure, it is difficult to read all of the "contents of the site" that has become enormous, and it is difficult to understand with "knob reading".

Therefore, we have compiled it into one book as an "Introduction Book".

Reference: The last day of the lower house election (illegal use of pensions)

http://www.youtube.com/watch?v=0FIZ9A1vkiU

References

Solve the mystery of earthquakes   Akira Ishida   PRC Publishing
Earthquake and its research   Mishio Ishimoto   Kokin Shoin
Road to Science   Mishio Ishimoto   Kajitani Shoin
Academic Language   Mishio Ishimoto   Kajiya Shoin
New interpretation of geological phenomena   Takuji Ogawa   Kokin Shoin
Exploring a new view of the Earth   Yukinori Fujita et al.   Aichi Publishing
Invitation to Geology   Yukinori Fujita   Tamagawa University Press
Earthquake Science   Keiichi Kasahara   Kousei sha
Dynamics of earthquakes   Keiichi Kasahara   Kajima Press
Earthquake Science   Hitoshi Takeuchi   NHK Books
Earth is a half-boiled egg   Hitoshi Takeuchi   Doubun Shoin
The law of becoming an original person   Hitoshi Takeuchi   Doubun Shoin
Earth Science   Hitoshi Takeuchi, Seiya Ueda   NHK Books
A new view of the earth   Seiya Ueda   Iwanami Shinsho
Tangshan Earthquake   Qian Gang   Asahi Shimbun
What is an active fault?   Yasutaka Ikeda, Kunihiko Shimazaki et.al   The University of Tokyo Press
What is a slow earthquake   Ichiro Kawasaki   NHK Books
Earthquake, plate, land and sea   Yoshio Fukao   Iwanami Junior New Book
The first history of geology and astronomy   Michiko Yajima et.al   Bere Publishing
The lie of seismology   Hiroshi Yamamoto   Kougaku sha
A huge earthquake occurs by hydrogen fusion   Hiroshi Yamamoto   Kougaku sha
God's Fingerprint (Up / Down)   Graham Hancock   Syouei
Predicting the end of the earth   John White   Mikasa Shobo
Anti-plate tectonics   Michihei Hoshino   EG Service Publishing
Tsunami Disaster   Yosiaki Kawada   Iwanami Shinsho
Earthquake   Kumiji Iida   Hokuryuukan
Unknown Underground High-Temperature Biosphere   Thomas Gold   Otsuki Shobo
Centennial Seismology   Tkanori Hagiwara   University of Tokyo Press
Radius of the Earth   Michihei Hoshino   Tokai University Press
Why do animals make noise before the earthquake?   Motoji Ikeya   NHK Books
Plate tectonics basics   Tetsuzo Seno   Asakura Shoten
Seismology   Tokuji Utsu   Kyoritsu Publishing
Japanese earthquake   Yasumoto Suzuki   Tsukiji Shokan
Earthquake and water   Junzo Kasahara et.al.   The University of Tokyo Press
Earthquake and Science   Izumi Yokoyama (supervised)   Tokai University Press
The lifetime of the island   Henry W. Menard   Tokyo Chemical Doujin

History of the Earth   Motonorii Shirao, Shoichi Kiyokawa   Iwanami Shoten
Surge Tectonics   M. Meyerhof et.al.   Kyoritsu Publishing
Earthquake   Sugiyama, Hayakawa, Hoshino   Tokai University Press
Kii Peninsula Earthquake Tsunami Data
    National Disaster Prevention Science and Technology Agency Center
Journey to the Earth   Japan Broadcasting Publishing Association
Paul Shift   Akio Asuka, Takeru Mikami   Gakken
Atlantis Research   N.F. Jirov   Tairiku Shobou

Author bio

Akira Ishida
Director, Ishida Research Institute (Doctor of Engineering, Kyoto University)

Born in Osaka in 1942, raised in Gifu Prefecture.
1960 Graduated from Gifu Prefectural Tajimi High School
1964 Graduated from Nagoya Institute of Technology Department of Civil Engi-
      neering
1966 Nagoya Institute of Technology Graduate School   Syuusikatei
1966 Assistant , Disaster Prevention Research Institute, Kyoto University
1968 Assistant, Department of Civil Engineering, Faculty of Engineering, Kyoto
      University
1974 PhD in Kyoto University
1975 Associate Professor, Nagoya Institute of Technology
1984 Professor, Nagoya Institute of Technology
1989 Nagoya Institute of Technology Retirement (Retirement Memorial Paper
      "Private Seismology" Announced)
1999 "Solving the mystery of earthquakes" self-published publication
2002 Established Ishida Institute of Earthquake Science
2012 Appointed President of Earthquake Explosion Society

book

Natural disaster science encyclopedia (partial writing) Tsukiji Shoten
Exercise hydrology   Morikita publication
"Solving the mystery of earthquakes-The earth is misunderstood"   PRC Publishing

Notice
 Earhquake Detonation Theory(part1 Basic) This book
 Earhquake Detonation Theory(part2 Advanced)
 Earhquake Detonation Theory (part3 Addendum)

Part2 Advanced
Chapter 1 New Earth Motion Theory / Crustal Movement (Sliding)
  Principle of crustal deformation (pole shift)
  Influence of the ice sheet in the polar region
  Dr. Thomas Gold's theory of crustal deformation
  Evidence for crustal deformation
  Frequent tilt (excursion)
  Disaster caused by a major flood
  Japanese flood legend
Chapter 2 Prof. Hapgood's achievements
  Pirirais Antarctic map
  Reason why Einstein supported
  Professor Hapgood's sincere attitude
Chapter 3 Evidence of the sinking of the continent and entering the polar region
  Sinking of the Atlantis continent
  Sinking of Mu continent
  Sinking of the Ramdia (Lemria) continent
  Meaning of discovery at Rio Grande Rise
  The history of the Antarctic ice sheet
  Divide and move the continent
Chapter 4 Interpretation of the Ice Age
  Traces of glaciers
  Ice Age mystery
  No global freezing / snowball
Chapter 5 Mystery of Table Mountain
  Discovery of kyo
  Polar movement and submergence
  Table mountain on land and undersea
Chapter 6 Traces of Earth Changes
  Dinosaur extinction cause (Hirayama theory)
  Reasons for extinction
  Biological extinction case
  Fossils of wood that penetrate the strata
  Dinosaurs and human footprints running away from the tsunami
  Solve the mystery of Easter Island Moai
  Meaning of deep earthquakes inland
  African Great Rift Valley
Chapter 7 Mechanism of the moon separating from the earth
  The theory of the birth of the moon

Solving the mystery about the moon
The birth of the moon
Earthquake on the moon
Appendix 1 Description of ancient civilizations (continents) listed in the Sun Law
Appendix 2 Mistakes in proof of continental movement
Appendix 3 Who made the moon (excerpt article)

Part3 Addendum
Chapter 1 Conflict of common beliefs
The ocean floor has not expanded
Contradiction of the Pacific Plate
Philippine Sea Plate identity
Failure of Hot Spot Theory
Dive even in the seabed mountains (?)
An earthquake commensurate with the distortion has not occurred
Fault dynamics with local force
Trampoline effect (?)
Chapter 2 Gas eruption
Mystery of Shiranui
Gas Collected at Fault
Seneca Gun
A lantern is burned with gas from the basement (Echigo Sanjo Earthquake)
Mystery of the Lake Nios Earthquake
Chapter 3 Ejecta
Flood Basalt Plateau
Mystery of Mud Volcano
Chapter 4 The foundation of the crust(①)
The earthquake blank area is a safety zone
Push and Pull Distribution in the Great Earthquake
Surge Tectonics
Reasons for large earthquakes in the mid-latitude zone
Relationship between earthquake and golden
Chapter 5 The foundation of the crust(②)
Earthquake Fossil
Gravity Anomaly (Free Air Anomaly)
Moseseffect and reflow phenomenon
Mystery of Apocalyptic Sound
Chapter 6 Solar system
Martian residual magnetic stripes
Evidence that there was an ocean on Mars
Fully cooled star
Chapter 7 Mystery still unsolvable
The mystery of all the couple's rocks
Luminous phenomenon in Italy

（英訳）巨大地震は「解離水」の爆縮で起きる

The cause of the earthquake is not active fault,
but is Hydrogen Implosion

2020年1月10日　第1刷発行

著　者　　石田　昭

発行者　　渡邉　義之

発行所　　一般社団法人 中小企業デザイン総合支援センター（DISC）
　　　　　（出版）〒486-0903　春日井市前並町 2-10-3
　　　　　（本社）〒451-0045　名古屋市名駅 2 丁目 34-17- 711

　　　　　Tel.052-766-6422　Fax.052-308-6620
　　　　　URL https://disc-or.jp/publish/